ODD WORDS, EVEN NUMBERS

A Melange of Words and Numbers

IAN PATERSON

Published by Thorogood
10-12 Rivington Street
London EC2A 3DU
Telephone: 020 7749 4748
Fax: 020 7729 6110
Email: info@thorogood.co.uk
Web: www.thorogood.co.uk

A CIP catalogue record for this book is
available from the British Library.

ISBN 9781854188878

Designed and typeset by Driftdesign:
www.getyourdrift.com

Printed and bound in Great Britain by
Marston Book Services Ltd, Oxfordshire

CONTENTS

Abbreviations

IE	Indo-European
Fowler	Modern English Usage (Third Edition)
GK	Greek
L	Latin
ME	Middle English
Ob	Obsolete
OE	Old English
OED	Oxford English Dictionary on CD-ROM (Version 4.0)
OF	Old French

For Dylan, Joe, Archie, Ava, Orlando and Lyla

INTRODUCTION

This book was prompted by an urge to demonstrate that an ability to work with numbers is a vital constituent of literacy. We often refer to literacy and numeracy as if they were two separate languages, the speakers of which cannot effectively communicate with each other. More particularly, we rarely treat numeracy as a requirement of literacy.

Perhaps this compartmentalisation arises as a result of the notion which we pick up very early on from the school curriculum, namely, that learning to read, on the one hand, and learning to count, on the other, are quite distinct activities with little overlap. The apparent lack of interaction between the two disciplines makes it easier for so many of us to go through our secondary education prepared to admit to being innumerate. It is not hard to come across folk who are keen to boast of this affliction regarding matters mathematical. A quick search on Google of the phrase "I can't do math" reveals more than 64 million results. And yet it is difficult to come across anyone who is proud to broadcast the fact that he or she is illiterate. Indeed, many of those who have reading problems devise cunning stratagems to avoid having to reveal their inability whereas the mathematically challenged very often go out of their way to trumpet the fact.

This concern is not merely one of impression. Sir Peter Williams tells us in his *Independent Review of Mathematics Teaching in Early Years Settings and Primary Schools: Final Report June 2008*, page 3, that:

"Since the National Numeracy Strategy (NNS) was introduced almost a decade ago, there has been considerable progress in the attainment of young learners in mathematics...Nevertheless, issues regarding the teaching and learning of mathematics remain, and the United Kingdom is still one of the few advanced nations where it is socially acceptable – fashionable, even – to profess an inability to cope with the subject."

A report in May 2010 by the Chief Estyn Inspector found that 53 per cent of adults in Wales had numeracy skills below the level of an 11-year-old.

A report by KPMG in January 2009 estimated that the long-term cost of children leaving school innumerate could be as high as £44,000 per person up to the age of 37, giving rise to a bill for taxpayers of £2.4 billion every year. Much of this cost arises from the fact that those who are innumerate are more likely to become unemployed or to drift into crime. In addition, there is the cost of providing numeracy support in our schools.

In an article in *The Guardian* in May 2010, Digby Jones points out that a third of the adult population cannot add together two 3-figure numbers.

A 2011 survey reported by a new charity, National Numeracy, shows that, of those assessed as having an ability at Level 2 (roughly equal to GCSE grades A to C), 57 per cent achieved that level in literacy, but only 22 per cent in numeracy. In February 2012 National Numeracy reported that the position is becoming worse in that almost half of the working-age population in England is barely numerate. Apparently, some 17 million adults in England have a mathematical ability equivalent to that of a primary school child.

There is a strong cohort of opinion that the study of mathematics in England should be made compulsory to age 18. In a report in June 2014, *Vision for Science and Mathematics Education*, The Royal Society advocated a baccalaureate system in place of the A-level system arguing that: "Mathematics has relevance not only across the sciences but also in arts and humanities and to people's everyday lives and further career aspirations." According to The Royal Society, only 13 per cent of young people in the UK study mathematics beyond 16 and it has been estimated that at least one in four economically active adults is functionally innumerate.

Some argue that universities should include a post-16 maths qualification in their standard entry requirements.

The Department of Education has gone some way to acknowledge such concerns and to address the trend by announcing in December 2014, as part of its commitment to raise standards, the introduction in 2017 of six new core maths qualifications. These have been designed to encourage more pupils to study beyond the age of 16 where, according to the Department of Education, only one fifth of pupils in England continue to study maths at any level after achieving GCSE – the lowest level of 24 developed countries.

Even more disturbing is the study by the Organisation for Economic Co-operation and Development, published in January 2016, entitled *Building*

Skills for All: A Review of England by reference to data collected in 2012, which found that young people in England are the most illiterate and nearly the most innumerate in the developed world. The OECD's report ranked English teenagers second from last out of 23 developed countries in numeracy; in literacy, the position was found to be even worse. They came last in a list of 23 developed nations headed by South Korea, Japan and the Netherlands. Of 16- to 19-year-olds in England, only 71.4 per cent are in formal education and training which is the lowest percentage in all of the developed countries looked at in the report. This goes on to tell us that England has more university students with weak literacy and numeracy skills than most countries.

Although pensioners and those near to retirement were among the highest-ranked of their age group, the prevalence of illiteracy and innumeracy is apparently not limited to young people. The OECD study goes on to say that there are an estimated nine million people of working age in England (more than a quarter of adults aged 16 to 65) with low literacy or numeracy skills or both.

We see, thus, a constant flow of criticism concerning the failure of the educational system to raise the level of mathematical skill of students in England as compared with other developed nations. One of the OECD's recommendations is that priority should be given to early intervention to ensure that all young people have stronger basic skills.

In his book *Innumeracy: Mathematical Illiteracy and its Consequences* (Viking, 1998) John Paulos emphasises how innumeracy pervades both our private and public lives and has a number of serious consequences including:

- a tendency towards indulging in "pseudo-science" and sloppy thought;
- a tendency to be misled by our own experiences;
- a tendency towards accepting dubious propositions or scams;
- financial ineptitude;
- hazardous gambling habits; a miscalculation in risk-taking.

Of course, there are other consequences, in particular the possibility that, at an early stage, educational development may be restricted with a consequential damaging effect on earning opportunities. Industry, in whatever sector, requires recruits who have learned the discipline and the rigour which an understanding of maths can bring.

With increasingly fewer unskilled jobs on offer, this situation is likely to have a greater impact than ever before.

Nor are the educated immune from this condition, as witness a court decision in Lisbon in 2008 when a judge conceded that a previous judgement distraining one-sixth of the petitioner's assets was too severe and, accordingly, "reduced" the distraint to one-fifth of his assets. Research published by Scott Maier in 2010 into how 2,000 metropolitan newspapers handled mathematical content over a three-month period reveals that journalists (who might be expected to have attained an appropriate skill level) take insufficient care as regards accuracy and were responsible for regular errors, often of an elementary nature, with a new type of numerical error identified almost every other day.

It might advance efforts to correct this extraordinary malady of the twenty-first century if the system concentrated, not merely on numeracy itself, but focused also on the role that the teaching of literacy might play in the teaching of numeracy. A person who can read may nonetheless, in some sense, be regarded as "illiterate" if he does not understand basic arithmetical concepts just as someone who is adept at mental arithmetic, but who cannot read, may be regarded as "innumerate" in the sense that he may be excluded from all those applications of arithmetic and numbers which involve words.

It is inappropriate to treat ourselves as "hard-wired" for innumeracy and to blame it on one's DNA. A geneticist at King's College London, Professor Robert Plomin, the senior author of a study published in the online journal *Nature Communications* in July 2014, has said that: "Environmental factors are primarily responsible for why people are better at one skill than another." The study goes on to suggest that about 50 per cent of the genes that determine how well children can read also determine mathematical ability.

There are many gradations of illiteracy and innumeracy. Is a person who can read and pronounce words but does not understand them to be treated as "illiterate"? Is a person who feels at home with those basic mathematical procedures necessary for everyday living to be treated as "numerate" even though he is not able to use fractions? What is the earliest age at which a person can be said to be innumerate or illiterate?

To give us a start in tackling such questions properly, we need greater definition. The New Oxford Dictionary of English defines illiterate as "unable to read or write" and functionally illiterate as meaning "lacking the literacy necessary for coping with most jobs and many everyday situations". It is this test of illiteracy which I am principally addressing. I refer to innumeracy in the same vein, namely, as a disinclination to make any effort to apply oneself to arithmetic procedures, coupled perhaps with a willingness, without any embarrassment, to admit to that fact. Such a propensity is effectively an admission, not merely of innumeracy, but also of illiteracy.

It is easy to make generalisations. It is also too easy to appear to be pious in all this. I am not an educationalist or a tub-thumping campaigner. I do not have answers to these questions nor as to how we can improve literacy or numeracy. What I believe, however, is that by avoiding the compartmentalisation of the two disciplines and by treating them as part of the same learning process, we would be taking a confident step towards finding solutions to this worrying trend.

One limited purpose I seek to achieve is merely to delight in the many ways in which the use of words and the use of numbers overlap and interact. It is, indeed, the central hypothesis of this book that we do ourselves and our children an injustice by harbouring the notion that words and numbers operate in discrete orbits whereas, in truth, drawing attention to the close interaction between matters numerical and matters literal in our everyday lives can assist the overall learning process and is, thus, an opportunity to be grasped and harnessed.

We find examples at a basic level to support this proposition wherever we look. On the one hand, we talk of "**counting** numbers" and "**account**ing for profit" and on the other we "**recount** a story" and "give a detailed **account** of events". A "teller" describes a person who counts money in a bank as well as a person who narrates stories. The very way we use our language thus indicates the close interrelationship between word and number.

The function of number words in any language is not merely to facilitate communication. Number words also give us the opportunity to think and to theorise about numbers on many levels. The language of maths and arithmetic enables us to fashion our thoughts and, in so doing, to progress. Without the means of engaging in such thought processes, science cannot flourish. Research on the Pirah, a small tribe in the Brazilian Amazon, has found that the tribe has no words for numbers. Their number words extend only to words such as "few", "many" and "some" so that they can understand only approximations and not specific quantities. This indicates that our ability to handle numbers to a meaningful level is not an innate ability. Rather, for such facility to become an integral element of our culture, we need to understand the language; to develop more effective methods of teaching it; to care for and nurture it and to ensure that it remains stable.

Mathematics demands precision and clarity and without a clear understanding of the **words** of mathematics and their correct syntactical usage, it is impossible to obtain a full grasp of the principles of mathematics or even of the basic definitions which are used as building blocks. The difficulty that some schoolchildren and teenagers have in understanding maths appears on occasions to reside in the fact that they do not understand the words of maths and are, for example, thrown into panic when confronted with terms such as "division" and "multiplication".

Much of the skill required for problem-solving depends on a facility to take the leap from one discipline to the other. We often refer to this as "lateral thinking". Take for example the following mathematical problem. In a knockout tennis competition, how many matches will be played to find the winner if there are y number of entrants? This can be worked out laboriously with pen and paper on a mathematical basis. However, if we were to treat the question more as one which requires logical rather than mathematical brain power we might be able to solve the problem instantly by recognising that, if there are y players in any knockout competition, the number of players who will be knocked out will be y-1, this being the requisite number of matches and the answer to the problem posed.

The delight that many hundreds of thousands of TV viewers continue to take in the process of moving to and fro between words and numbers is more than adequately demonstrated by the popularity of the TV programme *Countdown* which has run on Channel 4 from 1982, broadcast its five thousandth edition in March 2010, and is one of the world's longest-running game shows. *Des chiffres et des lettres* on which *Countdown* was based has been running in France since 1965 and can be viewed throughout the world on TV5.

There is no shortage of candidates for inclusion in a tome such as this where the intention is to emphasise the inextricable link between words and numbers. In choosing particular words, I have veered towards terms which have some mathematical significance and in choosing mathematical concepts, I have sought to make the entries easily accessible to those who, like me, are not mathematicians.

Indeed, this is not a book which requires anything more than a basic understanding of maths although for convenience I have included, at the end, a short glossary together with several of the more extended mathematical proofs.

Most of the entries have been selected to demonstrate the many ways in which there is an interplay between words and numbers. Indeed, *interplay* is an appropriate word to use here since the examples I have chosen (some slightly complex and some trivial) have been selected precisely because they provide a context for play whether through wordplay or by indulging in recreational maths. Notwithstanding an underlying political motivation, this book is intended to provide a series of diversions which I hope will generate a lot of enjoyment for all ages.

What all the entries have in common is that they illustrate and provide examples of the very many circumstances in which there is a crossover, a link, a correlation, a contrast, a confluence, an interchangeability or an interrelationship between words and numbers so as to provide ample confirmation that, if we are to communicate effectively, we cannot allow numeracy to play second fiddle to literacy.

I conclude with a big thank you to all who have helped me, particularly my wife, Linda, and the whole family.

Ian Paterson
March 2016

"We should not write so that it is possible to be understood, but so that it is impossible to be misunderstood."

QUINTILIAN *De Institutione Oratoria* (circa AD 93)

"According to Freud what comes between fear and sex?

... Fünf."

TED COHEN *Philosophical Thoughts on Joking Matters*, University Chicago Press (1999) and thanks to Cathleen Cavell and Joey Engel

1
THAT'S ODD!

Odd

The word *odd* has taken anything but a straight path on its journey to the twenty-first century.

The Old English word *odde* meant an angle, a point or the tip of a weapon from whence it took on the meaning of the point of a triangle and then, figuratively, a third man having the casting vote in a dispute. The word *umpire* is derived from *non-pair* (not even) or the odd man who takes on the task of being a referee.

By extension from its connection with the number three, *odde* came to connote any uneven number, namely, a whole number which when divided by two leaves a remainder. Reduced to a simple diagram this could be represented thus:

Fig. 1

– where the remainder "sticks out". This sense of the word *odd* is recorded as early as 1375.

The word in its application to individuals came to describe someone who is unusual or "sticks out" from the rest or behaves strangely. This is the sense in which Shakespeare uses it in *Love's Labour's Lost*:

"He is too picked, too spruce, too effected, too odd ..." (Act 5 Scene 1)

However, neither of the phrases *odds bodykins* or *od's bodikin* in *Hamlet* (Act 2 Scene 2) nor similar oaths originate from the word *odde*. They derive from foreshortening the phrase "God's body" in order to avoid profanity. Another example of this is the word *zounds* or "God's wounds" (*Othello* Act 1 Scene 1).

The term *odds*, indicating a difference, first appeared in 1542. Shakespeare used the word to indicate variously: superiority, advantage, inequality, differences, quarrels and probability.

Odds is now used mainly as a betting term to indicate the proportion in which the amount staked bears to the amount which might be won and we speak of "taking odds" and "laying odds". We also use phrases such as "it is odds on that", or "the odds are that", both of which refer to the chance or probability that a specific event will happen. We also use the phrase "over the odds" meaning in excess of the going rate.

In addition to its significance as a mathematical term, we use *odd* in many different phrases such as:

- doing things at *odd moments* or unplanned intervals;
- the *odd trick*, being the last and deciding trick at Whist;
- *odd coins*, indicating a small amount of cash left over – *odd* being slang in Ireland for loose change;
- *at odds*, meaning at variance with somebody or something;
- *odds and ends* and its extension during World War II to *odds and sods* which Eric Partridge in *A Dictionary of Forces Slang 1939-1945* (Secker & Warburg) defines as "men on miscellaneous duties";
- *odd jobs*, unconnected tasks done on a casual basis;
- an *odd lot*, a random mixture of goods;
- an *odd thing*, something rare or unusual;
- an *oddball*, US slang for an eccentric person or outsider;
- *odd* as in "odd socks". (The mystery surrounding the regular disappearance of one of a pair of socks after a machine-wash has, incidentally, been solved by a reader of *The Times* who, many years ago, replied to a letter bemoaning such a loss from another reader: "I know where his odd sock is. It is in **my** washing machine.")

What most of these usages have in common is an allusion to "sticking out", harking back to the very origin of the word *odd* so that, after all of its journeying, the word has kept its faith.

How odd it is that the word *odds,* though formed by pluralising *odd,* is itself a singular noun. Other such nouns with a similar treatment are *trousers, jeans* and *news* as to which see page 122.

The conjunction of the words *odd* and *even* throws up some surprises. Harking again back to Shakespearian times, *odd-even* (*Othello* Act 1 Scene 1) meant around midnight whereas in nuclear physics the phrase now refers to nuclei of odd mass number and of even mass number. The apparently oxymoronic phrase *even odds* (often referred to as *even money*) has an entirely different connotation referring to a bet which, if successful, pays winnings equal to the amount staked as well as the return of that stake.

Pythagoras wrote about the concept of odd and even numbers in Greece as long ago as 500BC and Euclid defined an even number around 300BC as "a number divisible into two parts".

A more up-to-date definition of an odd number is an integer (see page 24) that cannot be divided by 2 without a remainder. In mathematical terms, an odd number is a number having the pattern of $2n+1$ where n is an integer. This makes it easy to understand why zero is treated as an even number.

More even than odd

Why do we treat *even* in all its manifestations as more "favourable" than *odd?*

It is possible that the inherent nature of mathematical calculations favours evenness in that the result of multiplying an even number by an odd number (or by any number of odd numbers) results in an even number.

Also, of the three alternative ways of adding together odd and even numbers (O + E, O + O and E + E), two result in an even result and only one in an odd result. However, there are four alternatives since E + O should be included. Indeed, if we include subtraction and thus count all eight combinations of adding and subtracting two numbers, we see that there is no imbalance since there are as many odd results as there are even:

O + E = Odd   O - E = Odd
E + O = Odd   E - O = Odd
O + O = Even   O - O = Even
E + E = Even   E - E = Even

A determining factor in the preferential status of even numbers arises from the fact that our system is a decimal system based on 10 and that each threshold reached in the process of counting (10, 20 to 90, 100, 1,000 and so on) is an even number.

However, evenness has not always been in the ascendancy. Plutarch (ca. AD 46-120) regarded the number 1 as having divine attributes. Virgil (70-19BC) referred to odd numbers being "to the gods delightful" and in Shakespeare's Merry Wives of Windsor Falstaff says to Mistress Quickly: "I hope good luck lies in odd numbers... They say there is divinity in odd numbers." The number 1 continues to give rise to curiosity. Benford's Law, conceived by Frank Benford (1883-1948), tells us that in tables of naturally occurring numbers such as the highest mountains and the populations of the counties of England, the number 1 occurs as the first or leading digit with a frequency often greater than 30 per cent. However, statistically, we would expect each of the digits 1 to 9 to occur with a frequency of only 11.1 per cent, that is, $^{100}/_9$. A leading 9 is the least likely to occur. This is a phenomenon which has been hard to explain but is used to detect fraud since, where figures inserted in a bogus set of accounts fail by a significant margin to match the expectations of Benford's Law, there must be a suggestion that those accounts are fictional.

In contrast, the number 2 is seen as having characteristics opposed to divinity. Indeed, *deuce* is still used as a euphemism for the devil in phrases such as "what the deuce?" and "a deuce of a mess". How has *deuce* come to mean the devil? In a game using two dice, the word *deuce* has come to indicate the lowest and unluckiest score – possibly eliciting an exclamation of annoyance from its thrower. It is not difficult to see how such expression of annoyance (possibly influenced by *duus*, Low German for "the devil") came to have an extended meaning – where the devil might be regarded as to blame for that unlucky throw.

It is not clear when the number 13 (see page 108) first became associated with bad luck but it is possible that the seeds of this superstition can be found in the Last Supper and its 13 participants. Since then, the disenchantment with that particular odd number has led to our current fashionable preference for even numbers, encouraged no doubt by the positive notions conveyed by qualities such as *even-handedness* and *even-temperedness*.

We talk of *impairment* meaning "damage" or "loss" where *pair* means "even", thus giving rise to yet further conditioning.

Boustrophedon

Separating odd numbers from even numbers occurs on a daily basis with street numbering. We are familiar with the usual method of numbering houses and shops where they bear consecutive **odd** numbers on one side of the street and consecutive **even** numbers on the other side. However, that is not universal practice.

The numbering of some streets starts on one side using the consecutive numbers 1, 2, 3, 4 etc. and, at the end of the road, continues crossing over and doubles back on itself with a continuation of that series. We can refer to such a street as boustrophedon, meaning "as the ox ploughs" in reference to the fact that, on such a street, the numbering crosses back on itself resembling the pattern followed by an ox when ploughing a field.

Squaring the odds

Consecutive odd numbers starting with 1 have the remarkable quality that, wherever we stop counting, their aggregate at that point will always result in a square number (a number multiplied by itself once). Thus, the addition of the first two odd numbers, 1 and 3, comes to 4 which is 2 x 2 or 2^2 and $1 + 3 + 5 + 7 + 9$ equals 25 or 5^2 and so on. Why does this happen? The phenomenon can most easily be explained by an extension of the diagram in Fig. 1 on page 15 using a pyramid of boxes where every successive tier involves adding two extra boxes as follows:

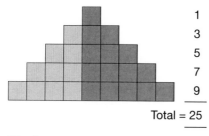

	1
	3
	5
	7
	9

Total = 25

Fig. 2

If we move the lighter shaded boxes in Fig. 2 and transpose them to the other side of the figure, we form a complete square as follows:

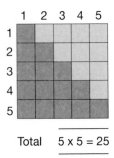

Total   5 x 5 = 25

Fig. 3

Cubes

We find a slightly different pattern involving consecutive odd numbers when we look at cubes (*cube* – a number multiplied by itself twice):

$1^3 = 1 = 1$
$2^3 = 8 = 3 + 5$
$3^3 = 27 = 7 + 9 + 11$
$4^3 = 64 = 13 + 15 + 17 + 19$ and so on.

A similar pattern to the square pattern occurs with numbers to the power of 4:

$1^4 = 1 = 1$
$2^4 = 16 = 1 + 3 + 5 + 7$
$3^4 = 81 = 1 + 3 + 5 + 7 + 9 + 11 + 13 + 15 + 17$ and so on.

Left-hand side page, right-hand side page

A maths teacher was writing a book dealing with various mathematical concepts, one of which was the difference between odd numbers and even numbers.

On one page he planned to explain the concept of an odd number and, on the facing page, the concept of evenness.

The teacher was eager to ensure that the left-hand side page was numbered as an odd page in keeping with its subject matter and that the right-hand side should, correspondingly, have an even number as its page number. The odd entry had to precede the even entry. However, the teacher had to abandon this plan. Why? In any printed book or pamphlet with two-sided text, the page on the left-hand side is referred to as the *verso* (from Latin *vertere*, to turn) and the right-hand side page is the *recto* (from Latin *rectus*, right). The convention (or, more accurately, the invariable practice) is to number the verso page as an even number and the recto page as an odd number. This arises as a result of the printer's practice of starting each chapter of a book on a recto page so that it will bear a page number which is odd. This practice of starting on a recto page may have grown not merely as a result of convention but to facilitate the production by printers of individual chapters or pamphlets since if each chapter of any printed matter begins on a recto there would be no need for the printer to renumber its pages.

If we envisage an offprint, it becomes clear that page 1, the recto, is the front page or the "face" of the document and page 2, over the page, is the "back" side of the front page.

If this hallowed practice were to be followed (as the teacher's publisher insisted), the verso would have had to have been an even number page and the recto an odd number with the result that it would not have been possible to meet the teacher's requirements.

To ponder...

Question A

At precisely 19.59 on 19 November 1999 there occurred an event which will not occur again for more than a thousand years. To be precise, this event can next be expected to occur at 1.11 on 1 January 3111. What is that event?

Clue 1: The self-same event in 1999 occurred in every time zone.

Clue 2: Try setting out the dates in numbers only.

The answer is on page 209.

Question B

A parallel event occurred at 22.48 on 28 August 888 which did not again occur until 00.00 on 2 February 2000. What is that event?

The answer is on page 209.

Question C

Odd will always be odd in that it bears an odd number of letters while *even* contains an even number of letters; but what is "never odd or even"?

Hint: Focus on the words of the question rather than on anything mathematical.

See page 209 for the answer.

2
NUMBERS, NUMERALS, INTEGERS, DIGITS, FIGURES, UNITS and AND

Some distinctions

In considering basic mathematical processes we refer to a variety of different but overlapping terms. We refer variously to *numbers, numerals, integers, digits, figures* and *units*. What does each of them mean?

Let us start with the question as to whether there is any difference in meaning between *number* and *numeral* – two words which in common parlance are often used as alternatives. We speak, for example, both of "Roman numbers" and "Roman numerals".

An understanding of the difference between the two words is perhaps best facilitated by looking at **number** as an abstract concept; that is to say, as having no material existence. *Number* imparts the idea of counting things or of quantity. The word might also signify the order in which things occur. In each case, we are juggling with a concept rather than with something concrete.

In contrast, the word **numeral** indicates a symbol which represents or denotes a particular number. Such a symbol is not abstract. It may consist of the Roman numeral M, representing 1,000, the Arabic 7 or any of the host of symbols used in other languages and systems to represent numbers. A numeral may have existence on the printed page or a computer or some digital read-out or it may present itself as a house number to be attached to a front door. A numeral is thus any mark or figure or symbol which represents a number or is used to express a number – particularly a single digit. In each such case, it is capable of being perceived.

This is not to say that the words *number* and *numeral* cannot, in many circumstances, be used interchangeably. Both words come from the Latin *numerus*, meaning "a number" or "reckoning", and from the Indo-European root *nem*, meaning "to apportion, divide, take or allot". Hence, we have words such as *nomad* (allotted land as pasture), *nome* (a province of Greece), *nomarch* (a senior Greek administrator whose title is easily confused with *monarch*) and a host of words with the *-nomy* suffix such as *agronomy, astronomy, economy, gastronomy* and *taxonomy*. We also get *nemesis* (a distribution of what is due).

An **integer** (pronounced with the emphasis on the first syllable and with a soft *g)* is any whole number including a negative number (and also zero). *Integer* has an interesting Indo-European root *tag*, to touch, as in the children's game of the same name. Combined with the Latin prefix, *in-*, meaning "not", this root provides us with the concept of being *intact* or *entire*. Hence, *integer* refers to an entire or a whole number. From *tag* we also derive words such as *tangent, tactile, tact, taste, tangible, contact, contagious* and *tax* (touches everyone).

The word **digit** from the Latin *digitus*, meaning "finger", is used to signify the first nine whole numbers and zero, resonating with man using his fingers to count. Hence, the phrase "single digits" is strictly tautologous. *Digit* derives from the Indo-European root *deik*, meaning "to show or utter", from which we get words such as *indicate, edict, judicial, prejudice, dictate, abdicate* and *vindicate*.

Figure comes from the Latin *figura*, meaning "a simple shape or form". *Figure* has many meanings. In mathematics it indicates a whole number and is often interchangeable with the word *digit*. It is also often used interchangeably with number, particularly in colloquial expressions such as "I am no good at figures" and "figuring something out". *Figure*, too, has an interesting Indo-European ancestor – the root *dheigh*, meaning "to form, knead or shape". Hence, we get *dig, ditch, dough* and *lady* or *la-dy* being a loaf-kneader (OE *Llaef-diger*) and perhaps also *paradise*, meaning "an enclosed or shaped park or garden".

Unit from the Indo-European root *oino* (see *one* on page 133) indicates, in mathematics, a single number as in "tens and units" – that is, in any number, the figure found on the extreme right.

Another instance where we have a choice of word occurs with the different expressions we regularly use to signify the process of adding one quantity to another. We variously employ several terms for this function – we talk of "9 *add* 6", "9 *plus* 6", "9 *more than* 6" and "9 *and* 6". Where do these terms come from and do they have any differences in meaning?

Add comes from the IE *do*, meaning "to give", from which we get words such as *donation* and *dosage* and the L *do, dare, datum* from which, in turn, we get the L *addere*, meaning "to join or unite", and its gerundive, *addendum*, meaning "that which should be added".

Plus originates from the IE *ple* (or *pel*), meaning "full, much or many". From *ple* we derive words such as *plenty, plethora, plenary, plebeian, plebiscite, plural* and *replenish*, as well as *surplus*, the prefix *poly-* and the conjunction *plus* from the L meaning "more". When we *add* to something the effect is to inflate it or make it fuller.

However, the precise meanings which we attribute to this everyday word (and its sister, L *minus*, meaning "less") in a mathematical context are not clear. Dictionary definitions of *plus* abound including "combined with", "in addition to", "added to", "increased by", "to which is added", "more", "more than" and a "summation of". Although we might expect to be influenced by the L *plus* meaning "more", this sense creates a syntactical difficulty since, in the phrase "9 plus 7 equals 16", the substitution of *more* for *plus* does not make sense. To incorporate the concept of *more* we would have to change the phrase to say that "16 is more than 9 by 7".

The fact that in the phrase "9 minus 7" we can indeed, without loss of mathematical or grammatical sense, substitute *less* for *minus* does not solve the dilemma as regards *plus*, particularly when there are several perfectly consistent formulations which meet the requirements of both syntax and consistency between *plus* and *minus*.

Treating *plus*, in a mathematical context, as meaning "in addition to" and *minus* as meaning "with the subtraction of" fits the bill. Alternatively, we might translate these terms respectively as meaning "increased by" and "reduced by" in each case without any ambiguity.

This brings us to **more,** from the IE *me*, great, from which we derive words such as *magnify, magnate, master, magistrate, magnificent* and *majesty*. We also derive the prefix *mega* – from the same root. The phrase "9 more than 7" is thus merely a synonym for "9 greater than 7".

And possibly comes from the IE *ant*, meaning "against, opposed or in front of", providing us with words such as *antagonism, antipathy* and *antipodes*. This short word thus has a more complex meaning than we might expect from a mere conjunction. When used, for example, in the title of Bertrand Russell's *Freedom and Organisation* it has the function not merely of linking the two concepts but of indicating that they are opposed to each other. The word *and*, of course, serves mainly as a conjunction between words and phrases. However, its pithiness makes it useful not only as a language tool but also in simple mathematics where, having the addition process in mind, we might colloquially enquire "What is 7 and 9?"

Curiously, there is one particular respect in which we treat *and*, when used in a mathematical sense, differently from the way in which we use it as a simple conjunction in everyday speech. When used as a conjunction between two nouns in ordinary speech, *and* commands a plural verb so that we say "Groucho and Harpo **were** brothers" and "time and tide **wait** for no man". There is nothing strange in that. However, when we give expression to a phrase using *and* in a mathematical context, we use the singular so that we say "7 and 9 equal**s** 16" and "7 and 9 come**s** to 16". This is because we are not treating the 7 and the 9 in this context as two separate items but are focusing on the phrase "7 and 9" as a discrete and singular constituent of the first part of a mathematical equation.

Calculation

The words considered in this chapter have the common factor that they each connote or anticipate some form of arithmetic *calculation* – another word with an unexpected etymology.

The word *calculation* comes from the Latin *calx*, meaning "chalk" or "limestone". In ancient Rome the facility for working out arithmetic calculations, such as we would now carry out with the use of pencil and paper, did not exist – nor could the manipulation of Roman numerals ever have been a straightforward exercise. However, the ancient Romans coped by using a counting board (a form of abacus) containing grooves on which small chalk pebbles could be placed and moved around for the purposes of indicating numbers and processing arithmetic operations.

The Latin for such a pebble was *calculus,* the diminutive form of *calx,* and the origin both of a branch of mathematics with the self-same name as well as the word *calculation* and its cognates such as *calculate, calculator* and *incalculable.*

It is no wonder that the image of the scientist busily chalking up equations on a blackboard is such a powerful one.

Counting

There are many words which commence with or include *count.*

The verb *to count,* meaning "to calculate or reckon", has given us *counter,* being a disc or object used in counting, and *counter* meaning "the surface on which the process of counting takes place". We also have words such as *account, discount,* and *compute.* Each of these derive from the L *computare,* to calculate, and the OF *conte* which, in the sixteenth century, came to be spelt *compte,* after the Latin, and so gave rise to the word *comptroller,* an erroneous spelling of *controller,* which nonetheless remains in use today in titles such as the Queen's Comptroller of the Household, an ancient position in the British royal household.

The word *counter,* meaning "opposite or opposed", comes from the OF *contre* and as a prefix generates scores of words including *counterfeit, counterfoil, countermand* and *countersign* – none of which has any etymological connection with the mathematical *count* although there are some respects in which a reckoning of some sort might be involved.

Count, indicating a member of the nobility, originated from yet another source. It comes from the French *comte* (with an *m* rather than an *n*) which, in turn, derives from the L *comitare,* meaning "to accompany", referring to a companion or part of the retinue of a member of royalty or of some other distinguished person. The land acquired by a *count* thus became known as his *county.*

However, counterintuitively, *county* is not cognate with *country* which probably has its origins in the L *contrata regio* (from *contra,* meaning "opposite") indicating the region spread out before one.

Countenance, meaning "demeanour, aspect or appearance", has yet another origin. It derives from the French *contenir,* to maintain (oneself).

3
SERIES AND SEQUENCES

Series

The word **series**, meaning "a row, a linking or an uninterrupted succession", derives from the Indo-European root *ser*, meaning "to line up or arrange".

From this root we derive a galaxy of cognate or related words including *desert* (in its sense of unjoining or abandoning and thence extended to indicate an area of arid abandoned land), *dissertation, insert, assert, exert, sort, sorcerer, assortment, consort, consortium* and *resort*. The word *seriatim*, meaning "one by one, in succession", is a combination of the Latin word, *series*, and the Latin suffix, *-atim*, which means "immediately" and is used to form adverbs such as *gradatim* (step by step) and *verbatim* (word by word). We possibly also derive the word *sermon* (being a connected set of statements) from the same root although an equally plausible alternative explanation is that *sermon* comes from the IE *swer*, meaning "to talk", from which we derive words such as *swarm* (buzzing bees), *swear* and *answer*.

A more obvious derivation from the root *ser* is the word *serried* as in "a serried rank of troops" referring to soldiers in close formation.

Serial, in the sense of successive instalments of a literary work, dates from 1841 and was used in connection with Charles Dickens' works. It was subsequently extended to radio plays and then to television programmes broadcast in a series of episodes.

The word *series* is a most unusual word for several reasons. Firstly, it is a Latin word in its own right meaning "a row or chain". Secondly, in English, it is, at the same time, both a singular and a plural noun. Although ending with the letter *s* it can be used in its unaltered form in the singular. Thirdly, *series* with the *s* removed does not constitute an English word, thus distinguishing it from words such as *species, news* and *means.*

In a mathematical sense, a *series* is strictly the sum of a group of terms occurring in a sequence and a **sequence** is an ordered list of items (usually numbers) which observes a particular rule determining each successive item to be added to that list. Simple sequences may employ any one or more of the of + - / x operators to enable us to work out a rule for determining the next number in the sequence. The first task in seeking to work out any mathematical sequence is to determine which of these operators appears most likely to be the key to the lock.

The word *sequence* derives from the IE root *sek*, meaning "to follow", from which we also get words such as *consequence*, the L *non sequitur* (a noun referring to something that is illogical or does not follow) and *segue* (a transition from one musical piece to another) now extended to any smooth transition in any discipline.

Nevertheless, the word *series* continues to be widely used to describe what is more properly called a *sequence*. A search, for example, on Google for "Fibonacci **sequence**" generated 511,000 entries and as many as 588,000 entries for "Fibonacci **series**" (see Chapter 26).

To ponder…

Here are some sequences to play with:

Question D
What are the next three in this sequence?

8, 5, 4, 9, 1, 7, --, --, --

Clue 1: Write out the above six numbers as words.

Clue 2: Scrutinise the first letter of each.

Answer on page 209.

Question E
What are the next three in the following sequence?
19, 28, 38, 81, 85, --, --, --

Clue 1: The third of the missing numbers will depend on whether you express the numbers from 100 to 199 as "**a** hundred…" or as "**one** hundred…".

Clue 2: Again, try writing out the above five numbers as words.

Answer on page 209.

Question F
What are the next two terms in this sequence?
3, 3, 5, 4, 4, --, --

Clue 1: Start at 1.

Clue 2: Start at *one*.

Answer on page 209.

Question G
**This sequence involves another connection between word and number.
Find the next two items:**
3, 6, 15, 16, 20, 18, 35, 40, --, --

Clue 1: Examine the numbers starting with 1.

Clue 2: Examine the number of letters in each number.

Answer on page 210.

The most basic example of a mathematical sequence is 0, 1, 2, 3, 4, 5, --, -- requiring no skill to solve other than the ability to count. Sometimes the apparent simplicity of a sequence can be misleading such as in the sequence 0, 1, 2, 3, 4, 5, 6, 7, 8, 9, 11, 22, --, --, the next two terms of which are 33 and 44 continuing a sequence of palindromic numbers (see Chapter 24).

Some sequences such as M, T, W, T, F, --, -- are mathematical neither in their presentation nor in the way their terms connect but merely require an experience of the world around us. Here are three further examples:

Question H
What are the next two items?
T, T, F, F, S, S, --, --

Clue 1: We could start with the letter O as the first in the sequence.

Clue 2: Concentrate on counting numbers.

Answer on page 210.

Question I
Find the next two items in this sequence:
F, S, T, F, F, --, --

Clue 1: This has nothing to do with **Question H.**

Clue 2: We are back to numbers.

Answer on page 210.

Question J
What might the next item be in this sequence?
disgruntle, disguise, disgust, disgusting, --

Answer on page 210.

While the individual words forming any sentence might be said to constitute a sequence, that sentence will have no rule (other than the rules of grammar) which could enable a reader to determine the next word in the sentence.

Question K
What sequences are indicated by the following times?
Thirty-six minutes and fifteen seconds to two o'clock in the morning.

Twenty-five minutes and four seconds to one o'clock in the afternoon.

The answers can be found on page 210.

In passing, what does the *o* in two o'clock signify? The phrase *o'clock* is merely a shorthand for the three words "of the clock", an expression used as early as 1389 by Geoffrey Chaucer in *The Canterbury Tales.*

Ghosts

The individual letters which go to make up any particular word could, in a sense, also be characterised as constituting a sequence. The next term of any such sequence might, in some cases, be capable of being determined with the assistance of a dictionary. The entries in a dictionary also constitute one long sequence, the rule for which is the rule used – in that particular dictionary – for determining alphabetical order.

This is the essence of that most entertaining of word games called Ghosts (or Ghost). Best played by two or three players, Ghosts involves the first player (let us assume there are only two) starting the game by announcing any letter of the alphabet. Player 2 must then call out his chosen letter to follow after the first so as to form a string of two letters, having in mind an English word beginning with those two letters. The process continues with the two players taking it in turns to add another at the end, at each stage calling out all the letters in the newly created string. On each successive occasion, the players must take care to avoid creating a dictionary word longer than three letters. If a player does create such a word then he loses a life.

If a player whose turn it is cannot think of a word to satisfy these requirements, he can either give up and lose a life or challenge his opponent to reveal the word he or she had in mind. The challenger loses a life if his or her opponent can reveal an acceptable word; otherwise the opponent loses a life. The first person to lose five lives loses the game.

The game is robust enough to allow for many adaptations so that, for example, the game can be played according to the rule that letters may be inserted not only at the end of the current string (that version being the traditional Ghosts) but also by introducing letters at the start of or anywhere in the middle of any existing string. That version of the game is called Superghosts.

Here is an example of a game of Superghosts:

Player 1: She starts with the letter **H** (1) thinking of *home*

Player 2: He follows with H**A** (2) thinking of *happiness*

Player 1: H**AS**   (3) thinking of *hassle* and being allowed to end a three-letter word

Player 2: **G**HAS   (4) having *ghastly* in mind with which he hopes to catch out his opponent

However, Player 1 has other plans for the fifth letter to be added:

Player 1: **A**GHAS   (5) thinking of *aghast*

Player 2: He now accepts defeat and the loss of a life since, by adding a T at the end, he would be ending a word. He is certain that Player 1 had *aghast* in mind so thinks there would be no point in challenging her.

However, had he been aware of the obscure word *fellaghas* (a guerrilla soldier) he would have been able to continue the battle by announcing the letters **L**AGHAS in the expectation of flummoxing his opponent. (6)

4
SPELLING NUMBERS

The letters of numbers

Are there any letters of the alphabet which are not used in spelling out the numbers from *one* onwards?

If we start with *zero,* then only two letters of the alphabet find themselves without a role to play in this venture. However, the letter D has to wait until *one hundred.* The ubiquitous letter A first appears in a *hundred and one,* although in US usage A has to wait until a *thousand* since 101 is expressed in the US as *one hundred one.*

Other letters have to wait much longer for their first appearance:

M first occurs in *million*
B first occurs in *billion*
Q in *quadrillion* and
P in *septillion.*

C has the longest wait, that is, until we reach *octillion* which is 10^{27} or 1,000,000,000,000,000,000,000,000,000.

This then gives rise to the following sequence or order of the first appearance of the letters of the alphabet in spelling out our numbers:

Z, E, R, O, N, T, W, H, F, U, I, V, S, X, G, L, Y, D, A, M, B, Q, P, C

The two letters of the alphabet which do not have any part to play in this are J and K. This is not unexpected since most of the large numbers derive from

Latin in which the letter J was unknown and in which the letter K (or *kappa*) was rarely used, being replaced in some words by the letter C.

The words of numbers

How many words do we need to expend in counting out in English each of the numbers from zero onwards in British colloquial usage?

We need only one word for each of the numbers 0 to 20. If we refer to 100 as *one hundred* and 1,000 as *one thousand,* and so on, then 20 is the last "one-word" number.

At 21 we reach the first number requiring two words. Two words will suffice until we reach *one hundred and one* which requires four words. To express numbers from 101 onwards we need at least four words although two or three will suffice when describing a quantity of hundreds, thousands or millions etc. such as *nine hundred* or *one hundred thousand.*

It is when we reach 121 that we first have a need for five words. Five words are adequate all the way to 1,101 when we first start to require the use of six words.

At 1,121 we start to require the use of seven words. This does not increase to eight until we reach the number 21,121.

We first need ten words with 121,101 and eleven words to produce 121,121.

The starting thresholds are therefore:

(1 word) **0**, (2 words) **21**, (4) **101**, (5) **121**, (6) **1,101**, (7) **1,121**, (8) **21,121**, (10) **121,101** and (11) **121,121** (which, by coincidence, is a palindrome and is divisible by 11 and 121, both of which numbers figure in this list).

Spelling cards

The following diversion may not hold the attention of adult readers for too long but it will interest children and, into the bargain, help them to learn to spell numbers.

It requires the preparation of four small cards – A, B, C and D, the fronts and backs of which are as set out on the next page. The black circles on the cards indicate punched holes.

The procedure is as follows. Present the front only of each of the four cards to your volunteer with a request to select any one of the numbers 0-26 appearing on the front of any of the four cards but without telling you what that number is.

Without revealing the back of the card at this stage, ask the volunteer to return the card from which that number has been chosen.

While you are holding that card ask the volunteer to spell out silently to himself the letters of the chosen number, one by one, and to indicate each successive letter by nodding his head. Each time the volunteer nods his head, you put the end of a pencil through the next hole in the card, starting with the top left-hand corner and moving around clockwise on the front of the card as if it were circular. It may be necessary to go round the card in this way more than once.

Ask your volunteer to tell you when he has completed the process of spelling out his number so that you will have pierced as many holes in the card as there are letters in the number he has chosen and indicated to you.

The fronts of the cards: **The backs of the cards:**

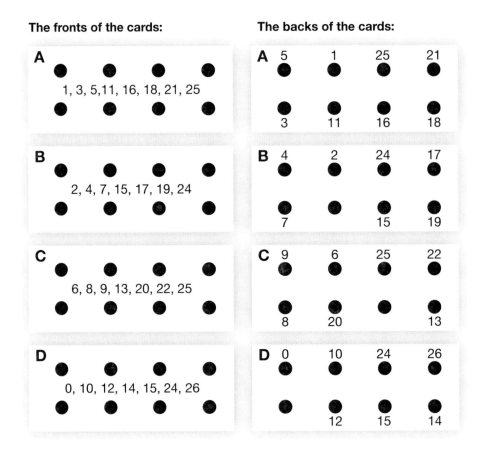

A

1, 3, 5,11, 16, 18, 21, 25

B

2, 4, 7, 15, 17, 19, 24

C

6, 8, 9, 13, 20, 22, 25

D

0, 10, 12, 14, 15, 24, 26

A 5   1   25   21
3   11   16   18

B 4   2   24   17
7   15   19

C 9   6   25   22
8   20   13

D 0   10   24   26
12   15   14

Fig. 1

When the volunteer announces that he has finished, you merely leave your pencil in the hole of the card last pierced and turn it over to reveal his chosen number on the back.

For example, if the chosen number was number 24 on card D your pencil will have ended up in the second hole of the first row of card D which, once you have turned it over, will reveal that number.

This diversion is a fine example of the close interaction between words and numbers. The process starts with a numeral which is converted into a word for the purpose, in turn, of counting out its constituent letters so as to enable them to be converted back to the original numeral.

5
SILENT LETTERS, SILENT NUMBERS

Silent letters

Such is the spelling of English words that many appear to contain letters which are redundant or not strictly necessary for their pronunciation. The following are some examples for each of the letters of the alphabet:

A marri**a**ge, inste**a**d, **a**egis, **a**isle, coco**a**

B de**b**tor, lam**b**, dou**b**t, su**b**tle

C ya**c**ht, vi**c**tuals, s**c**ent, indi**c**tment

D ju**d**ge, **d**jinn, We**d**nesday

E vin**e**yard, h**e**ight, ew**e**, giraff**e**

F fi**f**th, hal**f**penny, of**f**er

G **g**nat, **g**nome, diaphra**g**m, dou**g**h

H **h**onest, **h**our, w**h**ile, s**h**epherd, ex**h**aust, Dur**h**am, r**h**etoric, catar**h**, messia**h**, myr**h**, doug**h**

I fr**i**end, ne**i**ther, bus**i**ness, Le**i**cester

J Haj**j**

K knock, knitting, kneel

L salmon, would, yolk

M mnemonic

N damn, condemn, hymn, autumn

O country, people, leopard

P psalm, sapphire, cupboard, raspberry, corps

Q racquetball

R myrrh

S island, aisle, viscount, corps

T mortgage, often, hasten, bristle

U guard, gauge, dough

V luvvy

W two, sword, answer, wrapper, whole

X Sioux, billet doux

Y key, pyjamas

Z frizziness, rendezvous

In each of these words the omission of the highlighted letter would appear to make no difference to the way in which the word should be pronounced. In each of the words *aisle, corps, knock* and *myrrh* there are two unpronounced letters and in *dough* there are three.

Redundant letters

There are words which, despite the omission of particular letters, retain the same meaning. We can, for example, ignore the first two letters of *inflammable* without compromising its meaning since *flammable* also means "easily set on fire". Another example is *unto* and *to*. The little-used word *suasion* has the same meaning as *persuasion*.

Some words hardly change their meaning despite the extraction of a letter from somewhere within the word. For example:

crumple	rumple
especially	specially
splutter	sputter
steamy	seamy
stolid	solid
torturous	tortuous
venial	venal
wriggle	wiggle

Non-U

Why, where we spell the number four in the way we do, should we spell 40 as *forty* rather than *fourty*? All major dictionaries treat *forty* as the correct spelling both in UK and in North American usage but nonetheless the word is widely misspelt.

One suggested reason for the disparity between the spelling of *four* and *forty* resides not in any spelling convention but in the fact that the two words had two different roots. However, that theory is contradicted by the fact that, in Anglo-Saxon, *four* was *feower* and *forty* was *feowertig* which was merely an extension of *feower* using the OE suffix *-tig*, an old Dutch numeral indicating a multiple of 10. This suffix has transmuted, in English, into the suffix *-ty* to give us *thirty* and *forty* and so on and, in German, to produce, for example, *vierzig* (40). This suggests that *four* and *forty* have the same etymological origin and that it was merely as part of the common process of orthographic simplification that the *u* became detached from *fourty* much the same way as the *u* has been dropped in American English from words such as *colour* and *harbour*.

Fourty was spelt as such in Chaucer's time and the OED gives examples of its use up to 1698. However, its revised spelling as *forty* is used in the King James Bible, completed in 1611, and that may well account for why this simplified spelling took hold.

It is often unfruitful to seek an explanation of changes in spelling conventions, particularly as regards words that originate in Anglo-Saxon or Middle English. Right up to and beyond Shakespeare's time, spelling was a mercurial, even chaotic affair with little uniformity. Harmonisation did not begin to take hold until after the spread of printing which had the effect of encouraging publishers and printers to achieve greater uniformity in spelling as well as in grammar.

The letter H

It is revealing that there are so many examples of silent letters which involve the letter H since no other letter creates as much controversy. To better understand the letter H, the eighth letter of the alphabet, it is worthwhile delving into a bit of history.

The earliest known alphabet is the Semitic Ugarit alphabet, devised in Syria around 1700BC, consisting of 30 cuneiform consonant letters and possibly the precursor of the Phoenician, Hebrew and Arabic alphabets. By 1000BC, the Phoenicians had refined this alphabet to a point where it had become the model for half a dozen other languages including Aramaic and Greek.

The Greek alphabet was adopted by the Etruscans around 800BC and, in turn, the Romans adopted it and took it on as, ultimately, did all Western alphabets. The letter H originated around 900BC in the form of the Phoenician pictogram:

meaning "a fence" and probably pronounced with a hard *ch* sound. By 400BC, the Romans had come to depict this letter simply as H. However, the Greeks had long before dropped the letter H and by AD500 it had ceased to be treated as an independent letter and had come merely to indicate a sound, particularly in conjunction with other letters of the alphabet. As a consequence, the Romance languages have largely eschewed the letter, treating it merely as an aspirate.

Not only has the letter H's right to exist as an independent letter of the alphabet been in jeopardy; its mode of pronunciation, too, has always been (and continues to be) a source of confusion.

By AD200 H, as a sound, had all but disappeared from Latin and that is the reason the French language (derived primarily from Latin) does not use the H sound in many of the words imported from Latin which commenced with the letter H. The French use the letter in spelling H words but not in pronouncing them. Hence *hotel, habit, honnête* and *horloge*, for example, are all pronounced without recognising the letter H.

This has had a profound effect on the English language as a result of importing so many French words. In James Essinger's *Spellbound* (Robson Books, 2006) he explains the three main effects of this idiosyncrasy on the English language. One group of English words has dropped the initial H altogether such as *able* (from *habilis*) and *arbour* (from *herbarium*). Another group has kept the initial H but pretends that it is not there as in words such as *honour, heir* and *hour*. The third group of words comprises words originally spelt with a silent H but, by a process which took place in the sixteenth and seventeenth centuries, actually regained the H pronunciation. During this time, words such as *habit* and *harmonious* and *humble* and *humour* were pronounced without voicing the initial letter.

Confusion is compounded by the fact that up to the nineteenth century it was regarded by educated folk as quite proper to "drop one's Hs". How strange it is that this is now considered to be a bad habit indicating a lack of education.

Some of this confusion arises, no doubt, from the fact that pronouncing the letter H at the beginning of a word does not come naturally to our vocal cords. It requires, as an aspirate, more effort than pronouncing almost any other letter of the alphabet. However, the trouble with this explanation resides in the quaint pronunciation of the name of the letter itself. This has arisen partly as an overre-action to the chastisement we receive for "dropping our aitches". It seems that the spread of the non-standard pronunciation *haitch* is also the result of the influence emanating from Ireland where many Catholic schools teach that pronunciation in preference to *aitch* in a manner faintly reminiscent of a shibboleth.

The BBC pronunciation unit in October 2010 attests *haitch* as a legitimate form of pronunciation although *aitch* remains the standard.

Even the **spelling** of the letter H remains uncertain. In Shakespeare's era it was written as *ache*, the conventional form of *aitch* not being recorded until 1887. That ambiguity continues in that the BBC pronunciation unit uses both *aytch* and *haytch*, neither of which is a variation appearing in the OED.

Pronouncing numbers

The pronunciation of our numbers is also not without interest. We grow up as English speakers learning to count by rote from early childhood and without a thought as to why we pronounce our numbers in the way we do.

Pondering on this may well persuade us how odd it is that *one* is pronounced as it is. There is no hint of the letter W in the word *one* any more than there is in words cognate with *one* such as *atone*, *alone* and *only*, all of which are pronounced with a hard letter O. Indeed, *one* is the only English word commencing with the two letters *on* which is pronounced in this way. This is not so much a quaint pronunciation; it arises as a result of a particular dialectical variation, namely *wun*, which took precedence in the fourteenth century and caught on by dint of usage. Hence, we use an expression such as *young'un* to describe a young person.

Two also has an unexpected pronunciation. Whilst the letter W does appear in the word *two*, in this case we ignore it when we pronounce it.

Another number curiosity arises with the pronunciation of the adverb *eighthly* where the letter T, although appearing once, is pronounced twice and the letter H, though appearing twice, is pronounced only once.

Capitonyms

Some words, referred to as capitonyms, are pronounced differently according to whether or not they are being used to refer to a place or a proper name so that, for example, the following have different pronunciations or a different syllable emphasis depending on whether they commence with an upper or lower-case first letter:

Nice – nice	**August** – august
Reading – reading	**Job** – job
Polish – polish	**Mobile** – mobile
Tangier – tangier (appears in the OED)	**Natal** – natal

The wolhe wrod

Now it is wlel kwnon taht the hamun barin is adpet at raednig txet wihch prsenets iseltf (as deos tihs pragarpah) wthi msot of its wrods in the wonrg odrer amlost as esaliy as it can raed txet wcihh is seplt crtrocely. Cmabigrde Uvisenrity has fnuod taht as lnog as the wrods in any txet hvae tehir frist and lsat ltteers in thier crorcet psitooin the brian can mroe tahn esaliy coep wtih the tsak of minakg snese of the arppanet nenossne. By now you will hvae been albe to vriefy tihs pemnhoeonn for yuroeslf. Tihs itnersertnig osbrevtaion (mtso dficifult to tpye if you hvae an atuo-crorcet fcliatiy on yuor wrod porecssor) asries bceusae wehn we raed we fcuos frislty on the wolhe wrod.

Texting

In texting it is, of course, possible to communicate effectively (although not elegantly) notwithstanding the omission of letters from most of the words in one's message.

However, this may be at the cost of precision and clarity – witness the following shorthand devices for use in text messages, each of which has a possible alternative meaning:

lol = "laughs out loud" and "lots of love"
kos = "keep on smiling" and "kill on sight"
nc = "no comment" and "no chance"
xs = "extra small" and "excess"
afair = "as far as I recall" and "affair"

Silent digits

When looking at any particular number string it is not to be expected that a digit could simply be ignored or deleted from that string without making any substantive mathematical difference in the same way as a letter can be omitted from a word without creating, as we have seen, any significant difference to the way in which it is pronounced or understood.

And yet in one particular mathematical process (and no doubt there are others) this is indeed possible: the process used to work out the digital root of any number in which the digits 0 and 9 can be disregarded. What is a digital root?

The digital root (sometimes "digital sum") of any number is calculated by adding together all of its digits. If the result of this process is, itself, more than one digit long then the sum of those digits is found and so on until a single digit is arrived at. That single digit will constitute the digital root of the original number.

Hence, the digital roots of the digits 1 to 9 are 1 to 9 respectively. The digital root of 10 is 1 and of 11 it is 2. Of 23 it is 5. Of 79 it is 7, arrived at by adding 7 to 9 to form 16 and then by adding 1 to 6 to reach 7.

Digital roots can be used for a variety of purposes. For example, as regards any number, its remainder after dividing it by 9 will always be that number's digital root. We can, therefore, instantly recognise that the remainder left after dividing 148 by 9 is 4 because 1 + 4 + 8 = 13 and 1 + 3 = 4 which is the digital root of 148.

Digital roots can also be used as a means of checking whether the process of adding or subtracting has been carried out correctly. Let us take for simplicity the process of adding together a set of numbers. Using digital roots to check the addition process works because the aggregate of the digital root of a set of individual numbers is always the same as the digital root of the aggregate of those numbers.

Hence, if we add together 17 + 11 + 5 + 9 we get 42, the digital root of which is 6. Now, if we find the digital roots of each of those four separate numbers – namely 8, 2, 5 and 9 – and add them together, we get 24, the digital root of which is also 6.

If the two results coincide, as here, that does not necessarily mean that the addition process has been carried out correctly, but there is an 88 per cent chance that it is correct. What the system does do accurately is to indicate an error in any case where there has been an incorrect calculation. In that event, the two checksums will not coincide.

The process of using digital roots to check whether a calculation has been carried out correctly is intended as a shortcut to avoid the need for repeating the original calculation.

This is where the process of "casting out the nines" comes in. When seeking the sum of the individual digits of any number so as to find its digital root, it is possible to speed up the process by ignoring the digit 9 or, indeed, ignoring any two or more digits in the original number whose aggregate comes to 9.

So in finding the digital root of 9,372,094,491 we can:

- ignore the zero
- ignore the three 9s (which are equivalent to zero)
- ignore the 7 and 2 which add up to 9
- ignore the 4, 4 and 1 which also add up to 9

– with the result that the digital root of 9,372,094,491 can almost immediately be found to be 3 since after "casting out the nines" this is the only remaining uncancelled digit. All the other digits can effectively be ignored in this particular process as if they were "silent".

The method can also be used to check not only the correctness of any addition or subtraction of numbers but also in the process of multiplication and division.

"Casting out the nines" is not a requisite to finding the digital root of a number. It is merely a method of speeding up the process.

This checksum methodology, once fashionable, has with the advent of computers, smartphones and electronic calculators, grown into disuse. This itself is good reason to explain how it works. There are some relatively complicated explanations using, variously, algebra or modulo mathematics, but here is a short informal explanation.

In the process of adding digits together to find the digital root of any number, the presence in that number of either of the digits 0 or 9 will not make any difference to the result of that process. For example:

Line 1: the digital root of $58 = 5 + 8 = 13 = 1 + 3 = \mathbf{4}$

Line 2: the digital root of $589 = 5 + 8 + \mathbf{9} = 22 = 2 + 2 = \mathbf{4}$

– which shows that the inclusion of the **9** in line 2 makes no difference to the result since, in each case, the digital root equals 4.

This arises because attaching 9 in line 2 to the 58 from line 1 has the effect, when calculating the digital root of 589, of **reducing** the units from 3 to 2 in line 1 (that is by 1) and **increasing** the **tens** in line 1 by the same amount, that is, from 1 to 2. It is inherent in adding or subtracting 9 to or from any number that the sum of its digits will remain the same. This is further illustrated by looking at the first few multiples of 9, namely 18, 27, 36 and 45, where, with each successive addition of 9, the **tens** increase by 1 and the **units** reduce by 1 so that the aggregate of the constituent parts in each case, when added together, continues to come to 9.

Just as the order of the **letters** in a word need not affect our ability to identify that word, so the order of the **digits** in working out digital roots is of no consequence in arriving at the result. Indeed, the very exercise encourages us to carry out the process of "casting out the nines" in respect of any string of numbers by examining the digits in a non-sequential order.

There are other more frivolous examples in recreational maths where numbers can simply be ignored. For example, the fraction:

$\dfrac{16}{64}$	produces	$\dfrac{1}{4}$

– which can be reached both by the correct application of normal division and also by cancelling the sixes on each line.

Whilst "ignoring" letters in the pronunciation of certain words is very different from "casting out nines", the concept has sufficient equivalence to enable us to identify another respect in which there exists a connection between the way we manipulate words and the way we manipulate numbers. The fact that we might employ similar processes in the handling of words as we do in the handling of numbers creates another crossover and a further indication that the two disciplines are more properly treated as partners in the one.

6

NUMBER INTO WORD AND WORD INTO NUMBER

Number into word

Many everyday words, quite unexpectedly, have their roots in numbers or number words.

Artiodactyl is a mammal with an even number of toes on each foot where the GK prefix *artio-* means "having an even number" and *daktulos* means "finger".

There are many English words formed from the L prefix *bi-* or the GK *di-*, meaning "twice, two or double" (see Chapter 17), including the word *balance* which derives from L *bi-* and *lanx*, meaning "a scale". The word *diploma* originally indicated a sheet of paper folded into two and came to signify a form of state recommendation with its later extension to *diplomatic*.

Biceps (from L *bi-* and *-ceps*, head) indicates a muscle with two heads, and *bisect* (L *bi-* and *sect-*, to cut) means "to cut in two". *Bisect* might lead one to assume that the word *dissect* is formed from the prefix *di-*, but the double S serves as a clue that this is not the case. The word comes from entirely different stock, namely, the GK prefix *dis-* and *secare*, to cut. We might similarly be misled by *diameter* which bisects a circle in half; however, the word comes from GK *dia-* and *metron*, measure.

The word *dilemma* means "a situation in which both of two alternatives are unsatisfactory" coming from GK *di-* and *lemma*, premise. It now has a less specific meaning and indicates any kind of predicament, however many potential solutions may be in contemplation. *Diphthong*, indicating the elision of two vowel sounds, comes from GK *di-* and *phthongos*, sound.

Quadriliteral has nothing to do with geometry. It means "having four letters" and enjoys companionship with the words *uniliteral, duoliteral* and *triliteral* referring to words with only one, two or three letters respectively.

The word *quintessential*, meaning "the purest example or embodiment of something", is a surprise. What is its connection with five – a connection we expect from the *quin-* prefix? The word refers to the so-called fifth essence of ancient and mediaeval philosophy, after earth, air, fire and water, which was thought to permeate all of nature.

A *centenary* is used to mean a hundredth anniversary although in North America and New Zealand the equivalent term is a *centennial*, both of which come from L *cent*, a hundred. We also use the GK prefix *hecto-* to indicate a hundred, hence *hectare* meaning "100 acres". The prefix GK *kilo-* means "a thousand" and is used in words such as *kilogram, kilometre, kilowatt, kilolitre* and *kilovolt*.

A *soloist* is someone who performs alone from the L *solum, solus*, meaning "sole".

The months of September, October, November and December take their names from the Latin words for seven, eight, nine and ten respectively. How then is it that those months now represent the ninth, tenth, eleventh and twelfth months of the calendar?

The so-called Numa lunar year of the Roman Empire consisted of 12 months beginning with *Martius*, the equivalent of our month of March. The fifth month of the year was called *Quinctilis* after the Latin for five and the sixth called *Sextilis* after the Latin for six. *September, October, November* and *December* followed logically as the seventh, eighth, ninth and tenth months and these, in turn, were followed by *Januarius* and *Februarius* as the eleventh and twelfth months added to the calendar by Numa Pompilius in the eighth century BC.

However, it became evident that the Numa calendar was not fit for purpose and it underwent a continual process of change with regular intercalations of extra days into the year to give the calendar a more accurate correlation with the lunar year. Both Julius Caesar and his great nephew, Augustus Caesar, were instrumental in reducing the confusion inherent in the old Roman calendar. To recognise these contributions, the month of *Quinctilis* was renamed *Julius* in 44BC (that being the month of Julius Caesar's birth) and *Sextilis* was changed to *Augustus* in 27BC (the month in which Augustus Caesar had conquered Egypt).

It was one of Julius Caesar's contributions, as from 45BC, to reinstate the month of *Januarius,* instead of *Martius,* as the first month of the Roman year – this being the month beginning closest to the shortest day of the year. *Februarius* was also promoted to the second month of the year. Those changes were not accompanied, however, by any permanent change in the names of the months *September, October, November* or *December.* Originally named as the seventh, eighth, ninth and tenth months, they continued to retain their respective names despite being displaced in the order of the months to become the ninth, tenth, eleventh and twelfth months of the Roman calendar. That incongruity was acceptable to the Romans and their Julian calendar and has been embraced ever since despite the replacement of that calendar by the current Gregorian calendar.

Date into word

If you do not have a calendar handy but you want to know on what day of the week any date in the twenty-first century falls, here is a remarkable method for working it out and, in the process, converting the numbers representing that date into a word. There are many ways of finding out the day of the week for **any** date; however, they are more complicated than this one (adapted from Edward H. Julius' *Rapid Math Tricks and Tips*; John Wiley & Sons, 1992, p.49):

Step A: The first step in finding the day of the week for any date from 2000 to 2099 is to add together the following four numbers:

1. The number constituted by the last two digits of the year in question
2. That number divided by 4 (ignoring any remainder)
3. The day of the month in question
4. A special number according to the month in question

Jan: 0 (6 in a leap year)	April: 6	July: 6	Oct: 0
Feb: 3 (2 in a leap year)	May: 1	Aug: 2	Nov: 3
Mar: 3	June: 4	Sept: 5	Dec: 5

Step B: After adding together the numbers in 1, 2, 3 and 4 in step A, divide the result by 7 and work out the remainder, which will be one of the digits 1, 2, 3, 4, 5, 6 or 0. If the remainder is (1) that will correspond to **Sunday**, if (2) **Monday**, if (3) **Tuesday**, if (4) **Wednesday**, if (5) **Thursday**, if (6) **Friday** and if (0) it will correspond to **Saturday** thus providing the required answer.

Let us take as an example, 27 February 2020, that year being a leap year:

Step A: 1. The year   = 20
             2. 20 divided by 4   = 5
             3. The day of the month   = 27
             4. February's code   = 2
                                    Total = 54

Step B: Divide 54 by 7 to get 7 remainder **5** which indicates a Thursday

With a little practice this procedure can be learned as an impressive party trick.

Some measures

Despite the introduction of metrication in the UK by way of the Weights and Measures Act 1985 requiring metric units to be used when weighing and measuring goods at the point of sale, Imperial measures continue to be widely employed in the UK. Indeed, it is still lawful to sell draft beer and draft cider by the pint as it is to sell milk by the pint in returnable bottles. Furthermore, the UK is the only major country not to include metric units on road signs to indicate distance or speed limits. Regulations also allow for fuel consumption figures to be expressed as "miles per gallon".

It is clear thus that the legislation does not ban the use of Imperial units. Their use is, indeed, hallowed by the regulations which define those Imperial measures which may be used with metric measures as supplementary indications. Included amongst these privileged definitions are measures such as *mile, inch, acre* and *pound*. It is, therefore, essential to understand Imperial terms notwithstanding metrication, the more so since they occur throughout our literature.

The term *mile* derives from the *mille passus* or the 1,000 paces which constituted the Roman unit of 5,000 feet and is 142 yards shorter than the English mile.

From the IE *oine* or *oino*, we derive the Latin *unus*, indicating "one", and *uncia*, describing a unit of weight being a twelfth part. Hence, we derive the *ounce*. In the troy weight system, which is used in weighing gold, 12 ounces is equal to one pound. (By way of digression, troy weight is used to measure very small quantities and required the addition of tiny lengths of twisted wire to the balance. These strips of wire were called "riders" from which we derive the jargon, beloved of lawyers, indicating a clause or phrase which has been added to a draft document.) We derive *oz* as a useful shorthand for our *ounce* from the Italian *onza*.

From *uncia* also came *inch* (once spelt *ynche*), an extension of usage from weight to length which nonetheless retained the idea of a twelfth part – 12 inches making a foot. From phrases such as "to inch forward" or "he would not budge an inch" the word has developed a less precise supplementary connotation meaning "a very small distance" or "to a very small extent".

Acre originates from the IE *ag*, meaning "to drive or lead", from which the Latin word *ager* (a cultivated field) comes – possibly from the notion of driving cattle. Hence, we get words such as *agrarian, agriculture* and *acorn* (fruit of the field). *Acre* originally had the meaning in English of a ploughed field, subsequently coming to indicate the area of land which a yoke of oxen would be able to plough in the space of a day. Currently, *acre* indicates an area of land of 4,840 square yards.

The word *pound*, indicating weight, comes from L *pondus* (weight) and the abbreviation of pound, *lb*, from an entirely different Latin word, *libra*, meaning "pound" or "scales".

Imperial measures together with all weights and measures are in essence words used as a convenient means of describing a precise numerical quantity. We could describe the distance of a *mile* as "1,760 yards" or "80 chains" or "8 furlongs". The single term *mile* is a convenient shorthand signifying each of these. A word representing such a unit of measurement can be said, thus, to translate into a quantity or into a number to a level of accuracy of meaning far greater than can almost any other single common noun. That may be what is expected having regard to the fact that, after all, the very purpose of measurement is to provide exactness. In contrast, most other nouns when used alone will give rise to vagueness and ambiguity, being reliant upon their context and the use of additional qualifying words in order to provide any degree of certainty.

Terms of measurement are, however, notorious for having different meanings in different jurisdictions and they vary according to the measuring system being used so that, for example, a *nautical mile* is longer than a *statute mile* by some 800 feet and *pound*, used as a weight, changes its meaning according to whether you are referring to the avoirdupois, troy weight or apothecaries' weight systems.

On a scale of 1 to 10

The marked increase in customer satisfaction surveys has given rise to a proliferation of the use of the "1 to 10 scale". This is a widely used mechanism for assessing respondents' opinions not only in the consumer world, commerce and the arts but also in popular culture so that the phrase "on a scale of 1 to 10" has come into the vernacular. It is no more the reserve of the scientist.

In contrast, word-rated surveys require respondents to give their ratings by reference to a given series of words ranging from adjectives such as "excellent" to "abysmal". 1 to 10 scale surveys have an advantage over word-rated surveys simply because numbers are of universal application. Words used in survey questions can be misunderstood or interpreted in different ways while numbers create much less ambiguity and allow for more accurate measurement of results.

However, even a 1 to 10 scale survey can involve subjectivity and imprecision, hence explanations are often supplied as to what the researcher means by each step on the scale. Also a 1 to 5 scale or a scale starting with 0 may be employed.

In whatever way a 1 to 10 scale survey is fashioned, it ultimately operates by converting numbers into words.

More numbers into words

Take a pocket calculator with an LED display and type in the number 5537. Is that more or less than you were expecting? An odd question. However, you will appreciate its relevance once you have turned your calculator upside down.

When the calculator is upside down, you will see that each of the numbers 1, 3, 4, 5, 6, 7, 8, and 0 as they appear on a normal LED display will, more or less, reveal letters of the alphabet in upper or lower case. In the same order, these letters are I, E, H, S, G, L, B and O which are adequate to produce a good number of words in anagram play, particularly where the repetition of any of the letters is allowed. There is a list of some of those words on page 210 (**Question L**).

To ponder...

The following sheet of paper was passed around a class of mathematics students by their teacher with the simple request that the list of six numbers should be added together to find the total. Even with an electronic calculator, everyone got the answer totally wrong (**Question M**). Why was this?

6 NOS
998
999
988
908
869
899

Fig. 1

The explanation is on page 211.

Alphametics

Alphametics (a term first coined in 1955 by J. A. Hunter) is a popular form of recreational maths puzzle involving the translation of words into numbers.

We start, typically, with an equation expressed in words which together have some plausible (or, more often, implausible) message or significance. The best-known alphametic was created by Henry Dudeney in 1924:

$$
\begin{array}{r}
\text{SEND} \\
+ \text{MORE} \\
\hline
= \text{MONEY} \\
\hline
\hline
\end{array}
$$

The objective of alphametics (sometimes also called cryptarithms) is to substitute one of the digits 0 to 9 for each letter of the equation to make it work mathematically. The rules are simple. A number which is allocated to a particular letter must be allocated to that letter wherever it occurs in the equation and there must be no leading zeros.

Henry Dudeney referred to this kind of diversion as "verbal arithmetic".

Puzzles can be extended to any arithmetic operation including addition, subtraction, multiplication and division and to a base other than the base 10.

The answer to the above puzzle is:

```
  9567
  1085
 ------
 10652
 ======
```

The fact that this is the only possible answer makes this particular example more satisfying than an alphametic which has several possible solutions.

The attraction of this kind of puzzle is twofold. Firstly, there is the challenge of devising a witty or relevant word equation which has only one mathematical solution and, secondly, there is the challenge involved in working out the mathematical solution to the equation. There are several algorithms for this process (some available on the internet) but they spoil the chase.

Solving alphametics requires logic and often a lengthy process of trial and error. For example, in Dudeney's puzzle above, we start off as follows:

1. The M in MONEY must equal 1.
2. Hence, the M in MORE must also equal 1.
3. S + M must be greater than 9 so as to generate a carry-over. Hence, S must equal either 8 or 9.
4. The O in MONEY cannot be 1 (since M = 1) hence it must equal zero.
5. E plus O cannot equal 10 hence there is no carry-over and S must equal 9. And so on along similar lines.

To ponder…

Other alphametic problems require an entirely different approach. For example:

$$
\begin{array}{r}
\text{TABLES} \\
\times\ \text{E} \\
\hline
=\text{STABLE} \\
\hline
\end{array}
$$

To solve this, one must first recognise that there is a clue in the fact that the multiplicand, TABLES, has the same letters as the product, STABLE, slightly reordered. The answer is on page 211 (**Question N**).

Many alphametics have been created where the words perform in the same way as the transliterated mathematical solution. Here are some further examples with solutions on page 211 (**Question O**):

ONE	ONE	SEVEN
+ NINE	+ TWO	+ SEVEN
+ FIFTY	+ FIVE	+ SIX
+ TWENTY		
= EIGHTY	= EIGHT	= TWENTY

Devising alphametics with such accurate resonance is not easy. Here are two with less than a perfect connection but which nonetheless provide some fun:

MAUVE	GREY
+ RUSSET	+ YELLOW
= MAROON	= INDIGO

7
INDIVISIBILITY AND DIVISIBILITY

Solo vowels

What are the longest English words which are spelt using only one vowel?

There are many such words with 11 letters (including *abracadabra* and *razzamatazz*) and a good number with 12 letters including *recklessness, tarantarrara* (denoting the sound of the trumpet) and *invisibility* (which is allowable only if we treat the letter Y as being a consonant).

There are several 13-letter words including *invincibility* (again with the "Y blemish"), *effervescence* and the magnificent (but equally afflicted) *karma-dharayas* (a Sanskrit word meaning a compound word in which the first part serves as an attribute of the second as in *bookshelf* and *seatbelt*). (Curiously, quite a number of lengthy one-vowel words are terms used in linguistics, grammar or philology.)

Moving up a gear to 14 letters, we find the word *indivisibility* (which again has the Y but provides the segue for the concluding part of this section). We also have *loxolophodonts* (mammals with crested molars), *degenerescence* (tending to degenerate), *senselessness* and *speechlessness*.

Disinvisibility, morphophonology (the study of morphemes in linguistics) and *defencelessness* each have 15 letters.

The prize must, however, go to *strengthlessness* with its 16 letters. This is on the basis that *grottochronology* (16) (the use of statistics to define the extent of the relationship between languages) contains a Y, *preterperfectence* (17) (past perfect in grammar) is too abstruse and *Chrononhotonthologos* (20) is the name of a play written by Henry Carey in 1734.

Pre-occupation with words which have only one vowel is nothing compared with the discipline of composing poetry or prose from which the writer has, throughout the work, avoided one or more particular letter or letters. The name for such an endeavour is a lipogram from the GK *leipein*, to omit. The 50,000-word novel *Gadsby*, written in 1939 by Ernest Vincent Wright, and George Perec's 300-page 1969 novel *La Disparition*, both written as lipograms without using the letter E, are perhaps the best examples – notwithstanding the appearance, aplenty, of the letter E in the names of the authors.

We could, at a stretch, refer to the word *strengthlessness* as "being divisible by Es with only consonants left over". However, the concept of divisibility is more familiar to us in the context of numbers where we often need to ask ourselves whether any particular number is exactly divisible by another number.

Divisibility

The tests for determining divisibility in maths reveal an array of interesting techniques. They will often prove useful despite the availability of a calculator since some of these tests can be done in one's head more efficiently than on a calculator.

These techniques will also assist where the number to be divided is too long for your calculator. Whilst every number is strictly divisible by another, recreational maths is interested in division where there is no remainder. Here are some of the tests:

2 A number will be divisible by 2 if its last digit is 0, 2, 4, 6 or 8, that is, if it is an even number.

3 A number is divisible by 3 if the sum of its digits is itself divisible by 3; so, 1,945 is not divisible by 3 since its four digits add up to 19.

4 A number is divisible by 4 if the number constituted by its last two digits is divisible by 4; so, 177,**732** must be divisible by 4 because **32** is divisible by 4.

5 The number must end in 0 or 5 if it is to be divisible by 5; so 223,745 will divide by 5.

6 To be divisible by 6, a number must be even and the sum of its digits must be divisible by 3; hence, 77,784 is divisible by 6 because it is even and its digits add up to 33 which is itself divisible by 3.

7 In many maths books referring to the rules for divisibility, the number 7 is neglected. However, there are five different ways of applying a "litmus test" to determine divisibility by 7. They are each so remarkable that they deserve to be unfolded:

Method 1 (the Deduction Method): This is the most complex method and is useful for long numbers. Starting from the right, divide the initial number into sets of three digits. Then add together the numbers in the odd positions and deduct the result from the addition of the numbers in the even positions. If the result (whether positive or negative) divides by 7 (or is zero), the original number will be divisible by 7.

Example: Take 97,434,547

Step 1: Divide it into threes starting from the right. Hence: **(97)** (434) **(547)**

Step 2: Add the odd positions: **97**+ **547** = 644

Step 3: Add each of the even positions together (here there is only one): = 434

Step 4: Deduct one from the other: 644 - 434 = 210. Since 210 is divisible by 7 so, therefore, is the original number

Method 2 (the Doubling Method): This is an easier method and with two- or three-digit numbers it can, with practice, be done in one's head. Take the right-hand digit of the given number, double it and take that from the remaining digits of the number. Repeat as necessary. If the result at any stage (whether positive or negative) is divisible by 7 or is zero then the original number will be divisible by 7.

Example: Take 97**3**

Step 1: Double the right-hand digit, **3**, to get **6**

Step 2: Take **6** from the remaining digits so that 97 - **6** = **91**

Step 3: Double the last digit of **91** to get **2**

Step 4: Take **2** from 9 = 7. 7 is divisible by 7 and hence so is 973

Another example: Take **189**

Step 1: Double the right-hand digit, **9**, to get **18**

Step 2: Take **18** from the remaining digits so that 18 - 18 = 0 so that 189 must be divisible by 7

Method 3: This involves taking the right-hand digit of the original number and multiplying it by 5. Add it to the next single digit on the left and repeat the exercise. If the result divides by 7 at any stage so will the original number.

Example: Take 93**1**

Step 1: Multiply **1** (the right-hand digit) by 5 = **5**

Step 2: Add the next digit (3) to **5**, so 3 + 5 = **8**

Step 3: Multiply **8** by 5 = **40**

Step 4: Add the next digit, 9. 9 + **40** = 49. Since 49 is divisible by 7, so is 931

Method 4: In this method we multiply the left-hand digit of the original number by 3 and add to it the next single digit on the right of it. Repeat as necessary until the result is divisible by 7.

Example: Take **945**

Step 1: Multiply **9** (the first on the left) by 3: **9** x 3 = **27**

Step 2: Add to **27** the next digit on the right: 27 + 4 = **31**

Step 3: Multiply **31** by 3 = **93**

Step 4: Add the remaining digit to **93** so that 93 + 5 = 98. Since 98 is divisible by 7 so is 945

Step 5: If in doubt, try the test on 98 itself; so (9 x 3) + 8 = 35 which is divisible by 7

Method 5: If the number under scrutiny is of the pattern *abc,abc* (that is, its first three digits are repeated) then we can instantly recognise that the six-digit number must be divisible by 7 (and incidentally, also by 11 and 13). This is because any number with this pattern must be divisible by 1,001, the factors of which are 7,11 and 13.

This fact can assist in determining whether other six-digit numbers which do not follow this repeated pattern are divisible by 7. Take the number 971,950 as an example. The number created by the first three digits can be seen to be 21 greater than the number created by the second set of three digits. Since 21 is also divisible by 7 so must the original six-digit number be divisible by 7.

8 The number constituted by the last three digits must be divisible by 8; thus, 77,121,**096** can, at a glance, be seen to be divisible by 8.

9 The sum of the digits of the number in question must be divisible by 9. It follows that 117 divides exactly by 9 (see the explanation of digital roots on pages 46 to 48).

10 The number must, of course, end in 0.

11 There are at least four methods for testing divisibility by 11.

Method 1: Starting from the left-hand side take the individual digits in the odd positions and add them together, then take the individual digits in the even positions and add them together. Find the difference and if this is either 0 or it is divisible by 11 then so will the number itself divide exactly by 11.

Example: Take **352,049,797**

Step 1: Mark every alternative digit

Step 2: Add together those in the odd positions: **3** + **2** + **4** + **7** + **7** = 23 and then those in the even positions: 5 + 0 + 9 + 9 = 23. Since the difference between these two totals is 0, the original number 352,049,797 must be exactly divisible by 11

Method 2: This is a simpler method. Identify the unit digit on the extreme right of the original number and subtract it from the shortened number that remains. If the result is zero or is divisible by 11 so will the original number be divisible by 11. We can repeat that exercise until we are left with a number which we can recognise as being (or as not being) divisible by 11.

Example: Take 49,7**97**

Step 1: 4,979 - **7** = 4,9**72**

Step 2: 497 - **2** = 4**95**

Step 3: 49 - **5** = 44 which is obviously divisible by 11 and shows us that the original number, 49,797, is also divisible by 11

Method 3: The third method works with shorter numbers and relies on the fact that in any three-digit number, if the first and last digits, when added together, equal the middle number then the original three-digit number will be divisible by 11. By way of example, we might recognise that 495 meets this criterion (4 + 5 = 9 which is the middle digit). Hence, 495 must, therefore, be divisible by 11.

In the example in method 2 above, therefore, we would know without the need to perform step 3 that 49,797 is divisible by 11.

All this helps with problem-solving. Here is a simple problem which can be solved with the help of the above rules. What is the smallest ten-digit number containing each of the digits from 0 to 9 once only which is divisible exactly by 11? (**Question P**. The answer is on page 212.)

Method 4: See method 5 above in relation to number 7.

12 To be divisible by 12, a number must be divisible both by 3 and by 4.

13 We can find whether a number is divisible by 13 by a means similar to that in method 2 for number 11 above. Identify the unit digit on the extreme right of the original number and multiply it by 4. Then add the result to the shortened number that remains. If the result is divisible by 13 so will the original be divisible by 13. As in the case of 11, this procedure can be repeated until we are able to recognise whether or not the resulting number is divisible by 13.

Example: Take 10,25**7**

Step 1: 4 x **7** (7 being the digit on the right) = **28**

Add **28** to 1,025 = 1,05**3**

Step 2: 4 x **3** (the digit on the right) = **12**. Add **12** to 105 = 11**7**

Step 3: 4 x **7** = **28**. Add **28** to 11 = 39. This is divisible by 13 so the original number, 10,257, must also be divisible by 13

There are two further systems set out above in methods 1 and 5 as regards divisibility by 7.

14 To be divisible by 14, a number must be divisible both by 2 and by 7.

15 To be divisible by 15, a number must be divisible by both 3 and by 5.

16 To be divisible by 16, a number must be divisible by both 8 and by 2.

17 To be divisible by 17, we need to use the following method. Identify the unit digit on the extreme right of the original number and multiply it by 5, then subtract the result from the shortened number that remains. If the result is divisible by 17 so is the original number. We repeat that exercise until we are left with zero or a number which is easily recognisable as being (or as not being) divisible by 17.

Example: Take 16,47**3**

Step 1: 5 x **3** = 15. Subtract this from 1,647 = 1,63**2**

Step 2: 5 x **2** = 10. Subtract this from 163 = 15**3**

Step 3: 5 x **3** = 15. Subtracting this from 15 leaves 0 so the original number, 16,473, must be divisible by 17

18 To be divisible by 18, a number must be an even number and divisible by 9.

19 To determine divisibility by 19, firstly identify the unit digit on the extreme right of the original number and multiply it by two. Then add the result to the shortened number that remains. If the result is divisible by 19 so will the original be divisible by 19. As in the previous use of this method, the procedure can be repeated until we are able to recognise whether or not the resulting number is divisible by 19.

Example: Take 6,25**1**

Step 1: 2 x **1** = 2. Add this to 625 = 62**7**

Step 2: 2 x **7** = 14. Add this to 62 = 7**6**

Step 3: 2 x **6** = 12. Add this to 7 = 19 which being divisible by 19 means that the original number, 6,251, must also be divisible by 19

Aliquot and aliquant

The word *aliquot*, which occurs mainly in the phrase aliquot part, derives from Latin and means "several" or "a few". The phrase *aliquot part* in mathematics refers, in relation to an integer, to any of the divisors of that integer (other than the integer itself) which leave an exact or whole number. So that, for example, the aliquot parts of the integer 16 are 1, 2, 4 and 8. In contrast, the factors of 16 are 1, 2, 4, 8 and 16.

An *aliquant part* is a number which is **not** an exact divisor of a particular integer, hence 7 is an aliquant part of 18.

A Chinese puzzle

The following ancient Chinese puzzle provides an excellent example of how we might put to practical use the ability to use the above divisibility skills.

Two old friends were sitting together on a park bench watching the world go by when the old man turned to the old woman and asked whether she would consider him ungallant if he were to try to guess her age.

The old woman was intrigued and she agreed to his doing so. "Certainly," she said, "provided that, if you guess correctly, you will tell me how you did it." They had a deal and the old man asked the woman what the remainder would be if her age were to be divided by **3** to which her answer was "1". He then asked her what the remainder would be if, instead, her age was divided by **5**. "2" was her response. The old man finally asked what the remainder would be if her age were to be divided by **7** to which her answer was "6".

"Ah!" said the old man, "Then you must be 97."

The old woman was astounded that he had guessed correctly. How had he done so? True to his promise, he revealed the following simple method, adding that the maths behind it is based on a complex third-century Chinese theorem: "You multiply the first remainder by 70, the second by 21 and the third by 15 and deduct 105 from the aggregate."

Hence:

Division	Remainder	Multiply remainder
97/3	1	x 70 = 70
97/5	2	x 21 = 42
97/7	6	x 15 = 90
		Total = 202

– from which the old man deducted 105 to reach **97**

Mindful of how she would now be able to regale her grandchildren, she enquired of the old man whether it is always possible to find someone's age in this way. "Yes," replied the old man, "although you may in some cases have to deduct 105 more than once and sometimes not at all."

8
MATRICES

Matrix

A matrix is a square or rectangular array of numbers, entries or elements set out in rows and columns used to help solve problems where the relationship between its elements is crucial. The following is a simple 4 x 3 matrix:

$$\begin{pmatrix} 2468 \\ 1796 \\ 4732 \end{pmatrix}$$

Fig. 1

A more familiar term is *grid* or *table* which is a grating constructed by drawing lines to create uniform squares (as in graph paper) or to create uniform rectangles (such as in spreadsheets). A grid (unlike a matrix) is still a grid even if its cells have not been filled in.

The word *matrix* has an unusual plural, *matrices* (there are some other unusual plurals on pages 119 to 123). However, its main interest resides in its etymological origin which is a million miles away from anything mathematical.

The Indo-European roots *ma* and *amma* are redolent of the mutterings of young infants and we derive a host of related words from these roots including *mater, matter, material, mother, metropolis* (mother city), *matriarch, matron, maternal, matricide, mammal* (breastfeeder), *amour, amity* (and possibly also *enmity*).

Matrix is from the Latin being formed from *mater* (mother) and the Latin suffix *-ix* and means a breeding female. It subsequently came to indicate "the womb".

By extension, *matrix* came to mean a construct which enables something to be generated or developed. It could, therefore, be used to indicate a mould for creating things and, in mathematics, an array used to create solutions, an extension of meaning which is given additional resonance by the rounded brackets surrounding a matrix indicating a protective layer or enclosing framework. From *matrix* we derive *matriculate*, to become a member of or be admitted to a university, being a place of growth.

Routes

Taking the following 5 x 5 grid and moving from cell to cell, only upwards or to the right, how many different routes are there from point **x** to point **y**?

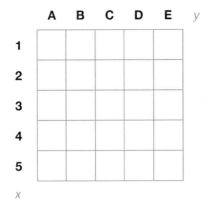

Fig. 2

It can be a time-consuming and messy business to work this out without a mathematical formula – so let us find one. Starting at *x*, cell A5, there is one route moving up column A from cell A5 to cell A1 so we insert a 1 in each cell in the A column to indicate this. Similarly, if one moves to the right along row 5 there is one route from cell A5 to cell E5 so a 1 should be inserted in cells B5, C5, D5 and E5 as shown in Fig. 3 below.

If the route chosen is from A5 to B4 then it is easy to work out that this can be achieved in two ways: A5-A4-B4 or A5-B5-B4. So we insert a 2 in B4 because there are two ways of reaching B4 from A5. With a little bit of further investigation, we come up with the formula that every cell (other than those in which we have already entered the digit 1) is the result of adding together the value in the cell to the left of it and the cell immediately beneath it.

So B3 = 3 (1 + 2) and B2 = 4 (1 + 3) and so on. As a result, we are able to complete the whole matrix as follows:

	A	B	C	D	E	*y*
1	1	5	15	35	70	
2	1	4	10	20	35	
3	1	3	6	10	15	
4	1	2	3	4	5	
5	1	1	1	1	1	

x

Fig. 3

The figure 70 thus arrives in cell E1 (point *y*) and that is the answer to the question first posed, namely, what is the number of possible routes from point *x* to point *y*.

If instead of going from cell to cell we were to manoeuvre along the **boundaries** of the cells as if the dividing lines were roads and the cells were blocks, then a 4 x 4 grid has the same result, mathematically, as a 5 x 5 grid where we move cell to cell.

Another variation on this theme is to see how many ways there are to spell out a particular word, again applying the rule of moving only up or across to the right.

	A	B	C	D	E	*y*
1	O	U	T	E	D	
2	R	O	U	T	E	
3	S	R	O	U	T	
4	I	S	R	O	U	
5	M	I	S	R	O	

x

Fig. 4

Out of bounds

The task of calculating the number of routes from point x to point y is made that much more interesting if one of the cells is made "out of bounds". What does this do to the number of available routes? To find the answer we need to allocate zero to the "out of bounds" cell and recalculate each of the other cells in the same way as we did above.

That procedure if done with pencil and paper becomes somewhat tedious. Instead, we can use an Excel spreadsheet. This works very effectively. Create a 5 x 5 grid and insert the value 1 in each of cells A1 to A5 and B5 to E5. Then insert, as a formula (using the equals sign), the value of B4, namely, = A4 + B5, and drag this formula to each of the other cells which will automatically result in E1 showing up as 70 in the same way as it does in Fig. 3.

Now select the cell which is to be treated as "out of bounds" and replace the formula in it with a zero. Each of the relevant cells will then automatically change its value including E1. Say, as shown in Fig. 5 below, that you have chosen D2 as being the "out of bounds" cell, then E1 will automatically re-register as 30.

	A	B	C	D	E	y
1	1	5	15	15	30	
2	1	4	10	0	15	
3	1	3	6	10	15	
4	1	2	3	4	5	
5	1	1	1	1	1	

x

Fig. 5

If we go back to Fig. 3 and shift the diagram clockwise by 135 degrees so that A5 becomes the pinnacle, you may notice that the configuration is no ordinary one. It looks like Pascal's triangle (see page 162) which has many fascinating applications including the extraordinary one of providing a mathematical method for solving the "out of bounds" problem described above – that is for working out the value of E1 when any particular cell is made "out of bounds". (**Question Q**: see page 212 for how this works.)

How many squares?

While we are looking at grids and matrices let us focus on another mathematical question, namely, how many squares of **any** size are contained in any square matrix.

Let us take a matrix of 3 x 3 to work out the answer to this question. In that matrix there are squares of 1 cell, 4 cells and 9 cells as follows:

9 of the smallest squares of 1 cell each
4 squares of 4 cells each
1 squares of 9 cells

– totalling 14 squares in all.

This gives us a clue as to developing a formula for the number of squares to be found in any size matrix. We simply add together the squares of each number from 1 up to the number of squares on any side of the matrix so that with a 3 x 3 matrix the answer is found by adding 3^2, 2^2 and 1^2 together: $3^2 + 2^2 + 1^2 = 14$.

In a 5 x 5 matrix there are thus 55 squares in total arrived at by adding $5^2 + 4^2 + 3^2 + 2^2 + 1^2 = 55$.

Lines

In a geometric sense, the shortest route between two points is, of course, a straight line.

The word *line* has its origin in the IE root *lino*, meaning "flax". This is the origin of such diverse words as *lineage, linear, streamline, outline, touchline, neckline, pipeline, headline, deadline, linoleum, linseed, crinoline, gridelin* (the colour of flax), *align* and *delineate*. It is also the begetter of the word *linen* which best helps to explain the connection between *flax* and *line*. Thread from flax was called *linea* by the Romans and came to be associated with what we now refer to as a *line* simply because when such thread is held firm at both ends it constitutes a straight line. Hanging linen out to dry on a washing-line illustrates the route this word has taken.

9
TIME AND NUMBER NINE

Nine or twelve?

The ancient Romans measured time by reference to the hours of daylight with the result that 6 a.m. was treated as the beginning of the day so that 3 p.m. would register as the ninth hour or the *nona hora*.

The *nona hora* was significant in early Roman times because it was the time determined by the Roman Catholic Church for the Divine Office mid-afternoon daily common prayer recital which came to be called *Nona* or *Nones*. (*Matins* is the daily midnight prayer session and *Vespers* takes place at sunset.)

The term *None* was adopted into Old English in its abbreviated form of *non* to describe daily afternoon prayers and it eventually transmuted into our present *noon* indicating 3 p.m. The meaning of *noon* gradually changed in the twelfth century to indicate midday since that more naturally corresponded to the time of the midday repast halfway through the day. Interestingly, the Church, over time, moved its mid-afternoon prayer recital to midday.

The word *noon* is just one of many examples of where our comfortableness with a particular word has overridden the illogicality of continuing to use it. Other examples are the months of September, October, November and December as explained on page 50 and the use of the word *key* to describe those ubiquitous plastic cards used to open office and hotel rooms and which no more resemble the instrument originally used to gain entry than does a modern electronic lock resemble the intricate mechanical device originally called a *lock*.

The term *None* has thus become associated with the number 12 despite the fact that it originally indicated 9 and has come to describe what the ancient

Romans would have described as the sixth hour. It has also spawned the little-used *forenoon* and the much-used *afternoon*.

The sixth hour is also interesting in that it has given rise to another example of where the time of day has been instrumental in spawning what is now a common English word. The Spanish word *siesta* originates from the sixth hour of the Roman day (*sexta hora*), which we now refer to as noon, being the hottest part of the day and hence an appropriate time for a snooze or a rest. When *siesta* came into English usage in the seventeenth century, it was used in the sense of the act of sleeping rather than the time to partake of it and it has retained that sense.

Following the same theme, *Nona/None* appears to have had another profound influence on our everyday language. In Middle English the word *noon-shun* (and its many variable spellings) was used to describe a midday meal. The word, indicating a retreat from the heat of the sun at noon, was probably a corruption of the earlier OE word *nuncheon*, meaning either "a lump of food" or "a pouring out".

An example of the effect of folk etymology can be seen here where the diffi-cult-to-pronounce *nuncheon* became *luncheon*, the letter N frequently being an agent for change in the pronunciation and spelling of words (see, for example, pages 145 and 146 and the transformation of *napron* to *apron*).

This is not the only example of where the way we express the time of day corre-lates with our eating habits as witness both the word *elevenses* to describe a morning drink and a variety of now possibly defunct terms using the word *four* to describe labourers' meal times at 4 p.m. such as the East Anglian *fourses*.

Some characteristics of number nine

Nine is no ordinary number. It is the highest digit and as such it has a central part to play in "casting out the nines" which, as we see on pages 47 and 48, has the useful adjunct of enabling us to determine the remainder when we divide any whole number by 9. This is because, as referred to on that page, the remainder of any number after dividing it by 9 will always be that number's digital root.

When adding together a series of numbers, number 9 also serves as a helpful method (once much used by accountants) of indicating that there has been a transpositional error where, in adding together a list of numbers, the total arrived at differs from the expected result by 9 or any multiple of 9. For example, adding together the four numbers 78, 92, 12 and 24 gives us 206. If, however, we had expected the answer to be 143 we might notice that this falls short of 206 by 63 which, being a multiple of 9, indicates that one of the entries might have been transposed. Indeed, we can soon work out that **92** should instead have read **29** which when corrected produces the expected result of 143.

In multiplying any number by 9, we generate a product the sum of the digits of which will always equal 9. This peculiarity is examined in Chapter 5 referring to digital roots.

All cyclic numbers (see pages 107 and 220) are divisible by 9 and, quite amazingly, each of the digits in the first half of any cyclic number when added respectively to the digits comprising the second half will come to 9. (In 142,857, for example, each of 1 + 8, 4 + 5 and 2 + 7 equals 9).

Furthermore, 9 is a square. It is also the only square which is the sum of two adjacent cubes, namely, $1^3 + 2^3 = 9$.

Another characteristic arises from taking any three-digit number where at least two of those digits are different and mixing them up to produce another three-digit number. Deduct the smaller of those two numbers from the larger. For example, 613 jumbled up could produce 361 and deducting 361 from 613 gives a result of 252 which is exactly divisible by 9. Whatever three numbers we choose for this exercise, and in whatever way we mix them up, the result will always produce a number which is divisible by 9. This works whatever the length of the original number we may choose because 9 is one less than the base of our decimal counting system.

This mathematical curiosity is the key to some interesting tricks, one of which is particularly effective. The trick starts by asking a volunteer to choose any number (but one where its digits are not all the same). Ask your volunteer to mix up the digits, as above, to produce a new one using all the original digits. So 895,623 mixed up might produce 385,692. You ask the volunteer to subtract the lower number from the higher to produce 509,931 but without giving you the answer. We know this must be divisible by 9.

You then ask the volunteer to select any one of the digits in the answer other than any zero. Say he or she selects 5 – the "chosen digit". You then ask the volunteer to disclose only the **remaining** digits, namely 0, 9, 9, 3 and 1 and in any order.

You are now able to announce the chosen digit.

From the fact that the aggregate of the digits in the result worked out by your volunteer (namely 509,931) must be divisible by 9 you are able to work out, with the minimum of effort, that his chosen digit must be 5. This is because $0 + 9 + 9 + 3 + 1 = 22$ and the nearest next multiple of 9 is 27 so his missing chosen digit has to be 5; that is 27 minus 22.

Hey presto! You can instantly announce the chosen digit with much flourish and amazement from your volunteer.

Paganini

The compère at a pantomime asks a question of a lone violinist who is reading a sheet of music on a music stand:

"What are you playing?"

"I'm playing Paganini," replies the violinist.

Whereupon the puzzled compère approaches the violinist, looks at the sheet of music, and replies:

"Don't be stupid – that's Page nine!"

10
NUMBER CONFUSION AND LARGE NUMBERS

Ambiguity

What is the point of communication if what we convey is not clear and unambiguous? To express ourselves in a way which is capable of being misunderstood, or which is likely to be misconstrued, can be much worse than saying nothing.

Although we expect mathematical terms to be precise, much of our everyday communication using numbers is open to misunderstanding and ambiguity even when we use a computer or an electronic calculator. For example, the letter I can easily be mistaken for the number 1 and B for 8. How many times, particularly in looking at alphanumeric passwords, do we ponder on whether we are looking at the letter O or the number 0? And 9 can be mistaken for the letter q and 5 for the letter S and so on.

When we hurriedly jot down numbers on a piece of paper there is the chance of confusion, particularly if that piece of paper has been rotated. Hence, we can, for example, confuse 3 with m or w, 4 with h, 6 with g, 7 with l, 8 with oo and 9 with 6.

The consequences of the smallest mistake can be serious, particularly in transcribing a bank account number. In 2015 Companies House (the Government agency responsible for the registration of companies) incurred a liability of £9 million as a result of erroneously reporting that a company, Taylor & **Sons** Limited, had been wound up whereas the company that had been wound up was an unconnected company called Taylor & **Son** Limited.

Billion

There is even greater room for error when it comes to very large numbers. The word *billion,* for example, is a word which has two established meanings which differ by a factor of a thousand.

In the US, *billion* (using the so-called short scale) has always meant 10^9 or 1,000,000,000, namely, one thousand million, or 1 followed by nine zeros.

However, until Harold Wilson determined in December 1974 that the UK government should use the word *billion* in the sense in which it is employed in the US, it was widely used in the UK, and in most English-speaking countries, to mean 10^{12} or 1,000,000,000,000 which is a million million in the so-called long scale.

Until the UK moved over to the US usage, 10^9 was referred to in the UK as a thousand million or a *milliard* which (as Jonathon Green explains in his *Dictionary of Jargon,* Routledge & Keegan Paul, 1987) was the origin of the term *yard* used in banking and finance to refer to 1,000,000,000 or 10^9. Since 10^9 now refers in the UK to a *billion* it follows that the term *milliard,* having provided sterling service for some 400 years, has become obsolete in the English language.

Likewise, the fascinating number *billiard* has also become obsolete. This term, before the adoption of the US usage, meant 10^{15} which, as explained below, now indicates a *quadrillion.* The word *billiard* has nothing to do with the game *billiards* and is not cognate with that word although both originated in France.

All large numbers from a *billion* upwards have alternative meanings according to whether the short scale or the long scale is intended.

There are currently many countries where a *billion* (or its equivalent translation) means 10^{12} rather than 10^9. France, for example, falls into the 10^{12} camp which creates grounds for confusion in Canada, where *billion* means 10^9 in Ottawa but 10^{12} in Quebec. However, the use of *billion* to indicate a thousand million in the short scale is now officially recognised by the European Commission.

Confusion can be further seriously compounded when we come to translate these number terms from one language to another. For example, in October 2010 the French press reported the prosecution of Jérôme Kerviel in France for forgery, unauthorised computer use and breach of trust and that he was ordered by the French courts to repay the sum of €4.9 milliards (or €4,900,000,000) by way of damages and interest to Société Générale. That was correctly reported in the British press as €4.9 billion.

But how would €4.9 billion be translated back into French? The equivalent of the English *billion* in French, as we have seen, is *milliard* so one stab might result in the correct translation, namely, €4.9 milliard or €4,900,000,000 which is 49 followed by eight zeros. It is possible, however, that the translation process influenced by the fact that that *billion* is used here in connection with the Euro, might assume that the original author intended the French *billion* and thus leave the phrase to be read in French as the same, namely, €4.9 billion. This would result in inflated damages of €4,900,000,000,000 or 49 followed by 11 zeros!

A literal word-for-word translation (for example, using an automatic internet translation facility) can create nonsense. Take the French sentence: *"La langue française employe le mot milliard mais maintenant cet mot n'est pas utilisé."* Translated into English this generates: "The French language uses the word billion but this word is not now used."

Yet another source of potential misunderstanding arises where, unknown to the reader, the English text containing the word *billion* was written prior to 1974.

The word *billion* meaning 10^{12} was coined in the fifteenth century by taking *million* and replacing its first two letters with the prefix *bi-* indicating two. This process defies etymological reasoning since the *mi-* in *million* is not a prefix nor did it have any meaning. *Million* derives from the Old French *mille* (a thousand) and the Italian *milione* or *millione* where the *-one* suffix indicated an augmentation. The word may even originate with Marco Polo, the Venetian, who wrote *Il Milione* in 1298.

However, the term *billion* in its non-US usage as 10^{12} does have some mathematical logic in that the word *billion* in that usage indicates $1,000,000^2$ where the power 2 reflects the 2 of *bi-*.

Similarly, a *trillion* originally indicated $1,000,000^3$ (or a million multiplied by itself twice) to reach 1,000,000,000,000,000,000 or 10^{18}. Another way of looking at this is to treat a *million* as consisting of 1 followed by **one** set of six zeros and a *billion* (that is, a non-US billion) as comprised of 1 followed by **two** (or bi-) sets of six zeros.

Remarkably, similar logic can also be applied to validate the word *billion* in its US sense of 10^9. A *million* consists of 1 followed by a set of three zeros and then by **one** further set of three zeros. A US *billion* consists of 1 followed by a set of three zeros and then by **two** (bi-) further sets of three zeros.

We can represent the short-scale usage as follows:

Word (short scale)	Prefix		000s	No. of zeros	Number	10^n
Million	mi-	1 + 1 = 2	2 x 3 =	6	1,000,000	10^6
Billion	bi-	1 + 2 = 3	3 x 3 =	9	1,000,000,000	10^9
Trillion	tri-	1 + 3 = 4	4 x 3 =	12	1,000,000,000,000	10^{12}
Quadrillion	quad-	1 + 4 = 5	5 x 3 =	15	1,000,000,000,000,000	10^{15}

...and so on

Fig. 1

Fig. 1 serves as a useful ready reckoner for determining how many zeros there are in any large number in short scale. Thus, as regards a *billion,* take the prefix *bi-* indicating 2, increase it by 1 to reach 3 which when multiplied by 3 gives us its nine zeros or 10^9. Likewise, with *quadrillion*. We take 4 (indicated by its prefix), add 1 to it to make 5 and multiply by 3 showing us that a *quadrillion* is comprised of 1 followed by 15 zeros or 10^{15}, thus producing the number from the word.

We can work in the opposite direction to find the word from the number so that if we take the number 10^{15} we could divide the 15 by 3 to reach 5 and deduct 1 from it to arrive at 4 which produces the prefix *quad-* and the number *quadrillion* or 1,000,000,000,000,000.

Even larger numbers

There are words for many larger numbers which frequent our dictionaries including *googol* (10^{100} or 1 followed by 100 zeros). There is *quintillion*, 10^{18}, right up to *vigintillion* (variously, 10^{63} and 10^{120}) and *centillion* (variously, 10^{303} and 10^{600}). However, there is no uniformity in the words used or their precise meanings. This is partly because of the differences between the short scale and the long scale. Whatever the reason, names for larger numbers are ambiguous and should be used with great care.

To avoid confusion it is better where possible to use the scientific notation (10 to the power) with a note as to whether the short or long scale is intended.

Where a number is intended to represent a physical quantity as opposed to a count, there is sometimes also the choice of using the prefixes adopted by the International System of Units (known as **SI**), which are set out as follows:

Word (short scale)	Prefix	Derivation	10^n	Number
MULTIPLES:				
one			10^0	1
ten	**deca-**	*ten*	10^1	10
hundred	**hecto-**	*hundred*	10^2	100
thousand	**kilo-**	*thousand*	10^3	1,000
million	**mega-**	*great*	10^6	1,000,000
billion	**giga-**	*giant*	10^9	1,000,000,000
trillion	**tera-**	*monster*	10^{12}	1,000,000,000,000
quadrillion	**peta-**	*five (1,000 to power 5)*	10^{15}	1,000,000,000,000,000
quintillion	**exa-**	*six (1,000 to power 6)*	10^{18}	1,000,000,000,000,000,000
sextillion	**zetta-**	*seven (1,000 to power 7)*	10^{21}	1,000,000,000,000,000,000,000
septillion	**yotta-**	*eight (1,000 to power 8)*	10^{24}	1,000,000,000,000,000,000,000,000
FRACTIONS:				
tenth	**deci-**	*L tenth*	10^{-1}	0.1
hundredth	**centi-**	*L hundredth*	10^{-2}	0.01
thousandth	**milli-**	*L thousandth*	10^{-3}	0.001
millionth	**micro-**	*L millionth*	10^{-6}	0.000001
billionth	**nano-**	*GK dwarf*	10^{-9}	0.000000001
trillionth	**pico-**	*Spanish peak*	10^{-12}	0.000000000001
quadrillionth	**femto-**	*Danish fifteen*	10^{-15}	0.000000000000001
quintillionth	**atto-**	*Danish eighteen*	10^{-18}	0.000000000000000001
sextillionth	**zepto-**	*L septem eight equal to (1,000⁻⁷)*	10^{-21}	0.000000000000000000001
septillionth	**yocto-**	*L/GK octo eight equal to (1,000⁻⁸)*	10^{-24}	0.000000000000000000000001

Fig. 2

The SI system facilitates the expression of very large and very small numbers by enabling the above prefixes to be applied to 22 different units of measure, such as metres and kilograms, either to express a multiple of such unit or a fraction of it.

10½
SOME MORE PREFIXES

Not by halves

It will be hard to find a trio of connected rhyming words, each having the same or a similar meaning, which more aptly reflects the diversity of the foreign influences which have so significantly shaped our English language, than the prefixes *semi-*, *demi-* and *hemi-*.

Semi- is from the Latin, meaning "half", as indicated in nouns such as *semiquaver* and *semicircle*. In adjectives such as *semi-detached* it means "partly" and in *semi-official* it has connotations of something indeterminate or to a small degree. In words such as *semi-conductor* and *semi-conscious* it indicates a position "midway between" and in *semi-allegiance* and *semicolon* it indicates something less than full. In words such as *semi-monthly* and *semi-annually*, meaning "twice a month" and "twice a year", the prefix has connotations of division into two – each such occasion marking one half of the whole period. In a knockout tournament the *semi-final* is the match immediately preceding the final (something less than the final).

It can be seen that the prefix *semi-* takes on many different shades of meaning. It is also frequently found in technical terminology. Indeed, as is shown in the following Google™ Ngram, *semi-* occurs much more frequently than does its Greek equivalent *hemi-*, which also means "half". *Hemi-* often indicates not merely an indeterminate half (as in *semi-*), but a particular half – either the top or bottom half along a horizontal axis (as in *hemisphere*) or a half-section along a vertical axis as in *hemicerebral* relating to one of the two halves of the brain.

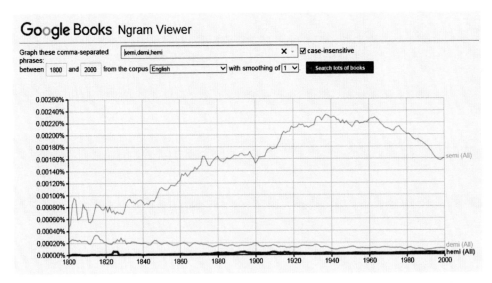

The third in the trio is the French *demi-*, which also means "half" or "half-size" and is used to indicate something having a partial, equivocal or imperfect quality such as *demigod* (a mythological being of partial divine origin). It is used in heraldry and military matters and also in describing fashion and costume. In *demitasse* it describes a very small cup.

All three of these prefixes come together in that delightful tongue-in-cheek construct coined in 1853, namely, *hemidemisemiquaver* – a musical note which is half the length of a demisemiquaver – which melds the three different linguistic influences into one word, so confounding those purists who would be critical of using a word which is constructed of, say, both a Greek prefix and a Latin suffix.

The richness of our language and the opportunities it provides for nuance can be demonstrated by the fact that we have yet another versatile prefix to convey the same idea, namely, *half-* from Old English, meaning "one of two equal parts of an object resulting from it being cut into two". *Half-* originates from the IE (*s*)*kel* from which we derive the L *scalpere,* to cut, and thence words like *scalpel, sculpture* and *shale* (easily split). It can be used in a wide variety of ways and is a powerful tool for creating new compounds. It can be used as a prefix with many adjectives and past participles such as *half-eaten, half-finished* and *half-hearted* where *half-* merely suggests a state which is less than complete rather than a mathematical fraction. *Half-dead* carries with it the connotation of being "nearly" dead rather than indicating any half-measure. When used with some nouns it more closely connotes the concept of being divided into two parts, hence *half-deck, half-door, half-mast* and *half-moon* whereas with others it indicates a much greater level of exactitude, such as in *half-crown, half-time, half-life, half-marathon, half-price* and *half-sister*.

The prefix *half-* may be versatile but it certainly has no pretensions of exactness.

Fowler points out that although the plural of the noun *half* is *halves*, we should refer to an apple being "cut in **half**" whilst, on dividing it into three or four parts, we should talk of it being cut into *thirds* and *quarters* using the plural form.

Fowler also tells us that the phrase "to act on behalf of" another is used in two main senses: "in the interest or benefit" of that person and "as the agent or representative" of that person. The word *behalf* is derived from combining *by* with *half* in its OE sense of one of the sides of an object cut in two. The word *side* itself was extended from the fifteenth century to mean opposing sides in a battle and we now also use the term to refer to competing teams in sporting events. When we talk about acting "on behalf of" someone we are "taking their side".

If we were to represent two or more persons, should we say that we are "acting on their behalfs" or "on their behalves"? Both constructions look odd, but despite the plural of *half* being *halves*, the first of these alternatives seems to have by far the greater support. If neither pleases you, then why not rephrase the sentence so as to refer to "acting on behalf of A and B"?

11
MULTIPLICATION AND NUMBER ELEVEN

Multiplying

As suggested in the Introduction, one of the many contributory reasons for low standards of numeracy is an inability to understand the **words** of mathematics. Some long words (like *multiplication)* can throw youngsters into panic as a result of which they are unable to carry out a straightforward mathematical calculation.

The term *multiplication* is indeed a confusing term with its many meanings and nuances.

The prefix *multi-* comes from the Latin *multi,* meaning "many", and originally from the IE root *mel,* meaning "strength or abundance". The second element comes from the L *plicare,* to fold, and from the IE *pel* or *plek,* to fold or bend.

The verb *to multiply* in its intransitive sense has the meaning of "to increase as a result of breeding" or "to increase by a substantial amount or to a substantial extent". In both cases the extent of the increase is vague and indeterminate.

In contrast, when used in its mathematical sense, the verb to multiply is transitive and has a precise meaning, namely, to perform the mathematical process often indicated by the letters n or x and the symbols · ╱ * whereby, in effect, a particular number (called the *multiplicand)* is **added** to itself a particular number of times (that number being the *multiplier)* with a result called the *product.*

The terms *multiplicand* and *multiplier* invite confusion. This is partly because, for mathematical purposes, the equation $a \times b$ gives the same result as $b \times a$ even though, in the first equation, a is referred to as the *multiplicand* and, in the second, as the *multiplier*.

The above definition of multiplication can also create confusion in that it involves the notion of addition (associated with the symbol +) whereas the multiplication process (indicated by the x symbol) suggests some other more complex kind of operation.

"Timesing"

Yet further confusion arises from expressing the equation $a \times b = c$ as a **times** b equals c.

What does the word *times* mean here and where does it come from? It comes from the IE root *da*, meaning "divide", so that not only does the multiplication process notionally involve addition but we see now that it also involves the notion of division.

This may be no less than we would expect since the division process is the inverse of multiplication in that if *a times b = c* then it follows that *c divided by a = b*. Nonetheless, it serves to befuddle.

Times came to be used as a term which could express multiplication because in the equation $a \times b = c$, c is equal to the quantity of *a* occurring *b times*. The OED shows us that the word *times* in this sense was used as early as c1380 by Wyclif.

Folding

The suffix *-fold* (from L *plicare*, to fold) is a powerful adjunct when used with numbers. *Fourfold*, for example, in addition to sounding so mellifluous, provides an economy of expression not easy to replicate.

Depending on the context, the suffix *-fold* can indicate either an order of magnitude or the concept of multiplication. Hence, the word *fourfold* can describe a quantity four times as great or four times as small. If promised that your investment of £100 will grow fourfold you would expect it to grow to £400 (100 times 4) but not **by** £400.

If there is a fourfold decrease, does that mean a reduction, say, from £400 to £100 (400 divided by 4) or to £80 (a deduction in the ratio of 4:1)? Symmetry would dictate that if a fourfold increase produces an extra £300 then a fourfold decrease should reduce £400 to £100 and that is what it should strictly connote. However, not all dictionaries agree. Sheridan's *A Complete Dictionary of the English Language* (1790) tells us that the term signifies "the same quantity added, as twenty-fold, twenty times repeated". Fourfold would thus require adding £100 to £100 four times giving us £500. *Collins Dictionary of Mathematics* also refers to a "repetitive process" rather than a multiplicative one.

Of course, the context will be relevant in all this. A fourfold increase in £100 indicates that £500 is reached whereas being repaid £100 fourfold indicates the receipt of only £400.

The suffix is used in conjunction with each of the single digits (even *onefold*) and is found in the OED with ten, eleven and twelve, but not with any of the teens. The words *twentyfold, thirtyfold* (but not *fortyfold*), *fiftyfold, sixtyfold* and *seventyfold* can be found but then not until we reach *hundredfold* does the suffix appear again. *Thousandfold* and *millionfold* are not uncommon. And, of course, there is *manifold*.

There is also the delightful Ulster word *sevendible* (probably now obsolete) which derives from *sevenfold* and indicates something severe or strong such as a good hiding.

Instructions to carry out any mathematical calculation must be clear so as to avoid any possibility of ambiguity. However, there is no uniformity when it comes to the precise meaning of *-fold* and this is no doubt why the term is not used with any gusto by mathematicians. It appears only in passing in *The Words of Mathematics* (Steven Schwartzman, MAA, 1994). It is used more in a vague poetical way as in "he repaid his debt a hundredfold" where the emphasis is merely being put on the fact of a significant increase rather than on any precise figure.

Simple instructions to carry out a mathematical exercise can often be ambiguous. Hence, the following kind of expressions should be used with care since, when applied to the number n, they can indicate a variety of possible meanings. A "fourfold increase in n" produces $5n$. "An increase of 400%" also gives rise to 5n, as do "a sum 400% greater than *n*" and "four times as much again". But "four times as many" indicates only 4n as do "an amount four times as large as *n*", "four times larger than *n*", "four times more than *n*" and "four times greater than *n*". Being repaid the amount "*n* fourfold" also means receiving 4n.

Some of these expressions allow for different interpretations and each is dependent on the context in which it is used so that in any case where precision is required it is best not to rely on *folding*.

It is no wonder that students sometimes find that multiplication is confusing. They are unlikely to understand the process merely from the meaning of the words used. Contrast the addition process, where it is far easier for schoolchildren to pick up the concept of adding one number or quantity to another from the word *add* since it is a more intuitive process than multiplication.

There is no easy way to convey the notion of multiplication merely by means of terminology so that any understanding must be conveyed by effective and skilled teaching. This tome has nothing to offer in that connection other than to remark that in any process of teaching it is often helpful to introduce some element of fun.

Multiplying by 11

There is an interesting way of multiplying by 11 which meets this endeavour.

Multiplying any **two**-digit number by 11 is so simple that there is no need to get out the electronic calculator.

Example 1
Take **34** x 11. Part the two digits 3 and 4 (producing **3 – 4**), add them together and insert that addition in the middle to get 374.

Example 2
If the addition of the two digits exceeds 9 (as in **46** x 11 where the addition of 4 and 6 produces 10) then insert the 0 of the 10 and add the 1 to the 4.

Hence:

Step 1: Part the 4 and 6 (producing **4 – 6**)

Step 2: Add the 4 and 6 = 10

Step 3: Insert the 0 in the middle to produce 406

Step 4: Carry over the 1 to increase the 4 to 5 so as to produce 506 which equals 46 times 11

We can use a similar procedure to multiply any **three**-digit number by 11.

Example 3
Take **614** x 11. Make the 6 and 4 the extremes with a two-space gap (so: **6 – – 4**) and insert between them, working from right to left, the result of adding the 4 to the 1 (5) and then the 1 to the 6 (7) resulting in 6,754. (The number of spaces inserted is one less than the length of the multiplicand.)

Example 4
This procedure can be used to multiply **any** whole number by 11. Taking **43,621** x 11, the steps are as follows:

Step 1: Make 4 and 1 the extremes of a new number **4 – – – – 1**

Step 2: Take each successive set of two adjacent digits in the number to be multiplied starting from the right-hand side. Add them together and insert the result in each case in the middle of those two digits

Hence with 4 <> 3 <> 6 <> 2 <> 1

we get: 4 **7 9 8 3** 1

where 479,831 is indeed equal to multiplying 43,621 by 11

If, in applying this process, the result of adding any two successive digits is more than 9 then add in the unit only and increase the next number to the left by 1.

Multiplying by 111

Even more fascinating (and in some cases even easier than multiplying by 11) is the process of multiplying any two-digit number by 111 without using a calculator.

Simply part the two-digit number with a two-space gap, multiply the addition of those two digits by 11 and insert the result in the middle. That is it.

Example 5
24 x 111

Step 1: Part the two digits to give 2 – – 4

Step 2: Add them together 2 + 4 = 6

Step 3: Multiply this addition by 11 (6 x 11 = 66)

Step 4: Insert the 66 between the 2 and the 4 to produce 2,664 or 24 x 111

Example 6
If multiplying the two digits at step 3 by 11 produces a number greater than 99, then increase the number on the extreme left by 1 so that with **65** x 111:

Step 1: Parting the two digits gives 6 – – 5

Step 2: 6 + 5 = 11

Step 3: 11 x 11 = **121**

Step 4: Insert the 21 of 121 to produce 6,215

Step 5: Increase the 6 by the **1** to 7 to produce 7,215 which equals 65 x 111

Another party trick

At this point, you might enquire as to the purpose of being able to multiply a number by 111 without using a calculator.

Not to be able to multiply by 111 in this way would deprive us of the opportunity to indulge in the following display of recreational maths.

Ask a volunteer with a calculator to take any three-digit number (ideally with each digit being different) and to write it down in its six permutations. Hence, 642 would have as its six permutations:

642, 624, 462, 426, 264 and 246.

The task you request from the volunteer is merely to add these six numbers together as quickly as possible using a calculator to produce, as here, the total of 2,664.

However, in a fraction of the time that this exercise will take him, you will be able to produce the answer in your head. To do this you need simply:

Step 1: Add the three digits together (here producing 12)

Step 2: Multiply the result by 2 (to reach 24)

Step 3: Multiply the 24 by 111 to reach 2,664 which can be done in one's head by using the method in example 5 above

Why it is that multiplying the aggregate of the three digits in the number by 2 and then by 111 produces the same result as adding together the six 3-digit numbers can be found on page 213: **Question R.**

Multiplication = Division

Reference is made above to the connection between the multiplication process and the addition process. Are there any instances where the result of multiplying two numbers gives rise to the same result as adding them together?

One simple instance immediately comes to mind, namely, 2 + 2 = 4 and 2 x 2 = 4. Are there any other instances? As Sam Loyd, the famous puzzler, has pointed out, there is, in fact, an infinite number of instances where this can prove true.

If we take any positive number (call it x) and divide it by x - 1 we arrive at the fraction:

$$\frac{x}{x - 1}$$

If we **multiply** this fraction by x we get the same result as we do from **adding** it to x as is demonstrated by the following three examples where x is taken in turn as 3, 8 and 761:

Column 1	Column 2	Column 3	Column 4	Column 5
x	x - 1	$\dfrac{x}{x - 1}$	Multiply col. 1 by col. 3	Add col. 1 to col. 3
3	2	1 ½	4 ½	4 ½
8	7	1 ⅐	9 ⅐	9 ⅐
761	760	761/760	762.0013158	762.0013158

Fig. 1

We can see from Fig. 1 that columns 4 and 5 produce the same result for each of the different values of x, even though in column 4 we are multiplying the two numbers in columns 1 and 3 and, in column 5, we are adding them together. For an algebraic proof see page 219.

Russian multiplication

The following is an unexpected way of multiplying any two numbers together by means of addition. Let us take 97 multiplied by 379 as an example.

We create two columns – the first headed by 97 and the second by 379. Find one half of 97 (ignoring the fraction), insert it immediately below 97 and continue with the same process until you reach 1. In column 2 we start by **doubling** 379, inserting the result below 379 and carry on the same process, successively doubling the previous figure until column 2 has the same number of entries as column 1.

Hence:

Column 1	Column 2
97	379
48	758
24	1,516
12	3,032
6	6,064
3	12,128
1	24,256

Fig. 2

The next step simply involves adding together those figures in column 2 of Fig.2 which do not have an even number beside them in column 1 so that we reach the following:

Column 1		Column 2
97		**379**
~~48~~	(even no.)	~~758~~
~~24~~	(even no.)	~~1,516~~
~~12~~	(even no.)	~~3,032~~
~~6~~	(even no.)	~~6,064~~
3		**12,128**
1		**24,256**
	Total	**36,763**

Fig. 3

This reveals the answer **36,763** which is what we expect from multiplying 97 by 379. An explanation of Russian multiplication is set out on page 221.

Endleofan

We must not end Chapter 11 without some explanation as to the provenance of *eleven*. In OE the word for eleven was *endleofan* meaning "one left over" and composed of *end*, meaning "one", and *leofan* from the IE root *leik*, to leave. Eleven is thus based on the notion of being the number which, after 10 has been subtracted, leaves us with 1.

Twelve has a similar logic. The word for twelve in OE was *twelf* from *twa* (two) and *lif* (left over) indicating the number which, after 10 has been subtracted, leaves 2.

Why all the other seven numbers in the teens (an inflected form of *ten*) follow a different pattern is not clear.

12
DOZEN

Why dozen?

Why do we need the word *dozen* when we have the perfectly adequate *twelve*?

Dozen comes from the OF *dozeine* which in turn originates from the L *duodecim* where *duo* is two and *decim* ten. And yet, *dozen* once signified a group of **approximately** 12, so that in the *New Enlarged Dictionary of the English Language* (1836) the word is defined as: "What is equal to twelve, thirteen or fourteen being sometimes given for the dozen."

Dozen is still ambiguous in that we refer to a *long dozen* meaning 13 or a *baker's dozen* consisting of 13 loaves. There are many explanations for this expression, the most likely harking back to the fifteenth-century practice of bakers providing one extra loaf so as to avoid the possibility of being in breach of legal requirements regarding weight. Other theories refer to the practice of providing the extra loaf by way of the retailer's profit, thus taking a leaf out of the book of printers who practised the same custom with their printed matter.

A *gross* however, is a more exact term meaning precisely a dozen dozen or 144 and coming from the French *grosse douzaine* which is the origin of the word *grocer* being a merchant who sold his wares "by the gross". This is a well-established usage, the Company of Grossers having been founded in 1345 and changing its name in 1376 to the Company of Grocers of London. (We may imagine that they had been desperate to incorporate just a few months earlier where 1344 coincides with **112 dozen**.)

A *great gross* equals 1,728 which is equal to 12 x 12 x 12 or 12^3.

Let us now get back to the original question. A *dozen* is not a number. It signi-fies a set or group or collection of 12 items of a like kind or having a common quality. It is also often used as an approximation as in phrases such as "I've told you a dozen times".

It is not to be confused with the contest known as The Dozens in which two persons engage in a slanging match, hurling insults and invective at each other until one of them, either out of frustration or lack of patience, strikes his opponent who thereby wins the contest. Although the contestants may well have been talking "nineteen to the dozen", the contest has nothing to do with the numerical dozen since it probably originates from the verb *bulldoze*.

What language?

Words such as *main, pain, chat, chair, dent, dire, bride* and *ride* are easy to read and have a clear meaning in everyday usage. However, they are but a few examples of English words which have an entirely different pronunciation and an entirely different meaning when used as part of the French language – and no doubt in some other languages. We need to know the language of the word in question in order to determine its meaning.

We need the same information when interpreting numbers. The numbers 11, 12, 25, 38 and 41, for example, have a clear enough meaning assuming that the "appropriate language" is the decimal system.

However, those numbers have a very different significance if we read them in another notation, for example in the binary notation (base 2).

What does it mean when we talk of base 2, base 3 and so on?

The system with which we are most familiar is the decimal system (or base 10) using the ten digits 0 to 9. This enables us to write numbers by indicating a given number of units (on the extreme right), a given number of 10s in the next space to the left and a given number of 100s in the next space along and so on.

Hence, the number 613 is made up of:

Multiplicand x Multiplier

6 x 100	=	600	or	6×10^2	
1 x 10	=	10	or	1×10^1	and
3 x 1	=	3	or	3×10^0	
Total		**613**			

For larger numbers in base 10, we simply carry on enlarging the multiplier by a factor of 10.

Let us take another decimal example displayed in a different way. The decimal number 7,356, for example, can be depicted as follows:

1,000s	100s	10s	1s
7	3	5	6

We probably use the decimal system today because primitive man's most practical system of counting would have been to rely on his ten fingers. However, there are many other notation systems which have been used throughout the world, some of which (for example base 2 or binary notation and base 16 or hexadecimal notation) are currently employed in programming computers.

The binary system uses only the two digits 0 and 1. In this system, the number 1011011, for example, is equal to 91 in the decimal system. It is constructed as follows:

64s	32s	16s	8s	4s	2s	1s
1	0	1	1	0	1	1

That is:

Multiplicand x Multiplier

1	x	64	= 64	or	1×2^6	
0	x	32	= 0	or	0×2^5	
1	x	16	= 16	or	1×2^4	
1	x	8	= 8	or	1×2^3	
0	x	4	= 0	or	0×2^2	
1	x	2	= 2	or	1×2^1	and
1	x	1	= 1	or	1×2^0	

Total **91**

It can be seen that in base 2 the multiplier is increased by a factor of 2 on each occasion as opposed to 10 in the decimal system.

Some applications of the binary system are described on page 112 regarding the game Nim and on page 221 in regard to Russian multiplication.

Duodecimals

What is surprising, at least at first blush, is that there have been many advocates of the duodecimal system, which is the notation system that operates in base 12.

For example, the decimal number 1,910 when expressed in the duodecimal notation is represented as 1,132 and arrived at as follows:

1,728s	144s	12s	1s	
1	1	3	2	or

Multiplicand x Multiplier

1	x	1,728	= 1,728	or	1×12^3	
1	x	144	= 144	or	1×12^2	
3	x	12	= 36	or	3×12^1	and
2	x	1	= 2	or	2×12^0	

Total **1,910**

It is argued by protagonists of the duodecimal system that it is superior to the decimal system. One compelling argument is that it makes it much easier to calculate measurements in feet and inches. If the task, for example, were to find the aggregate length of two pieces of rope of 5 feet 7 inches and 7 feet 6 inches, one approach using the decimal system would be to convert each measurement into inches as follows:

	Inches
5 feet 7 inches: 5 x 12 = 60 add in the 7 inches	= 67
7 feet 6 inches: 7 x 12 = 84 add in the 6 inches	= 90
Total	157

When converted back into feet and inches, 157 equals 13 feet 1 inch arrived at by dividing 157 by 12 (to reach 13) and calculating the remainder (namely,1).

This calculation takes time whereas by using the duodecimal system we merely add 57 (from 5 feet 7 inches) to 76 (from 7 feet 6 inches) to get 131 which instantly converts to 13 feet 1 inch, thus requiring one calculation rather than six.

It is further argued in favour of the duodecimal system that 120 has the factors 1, 2, 3, 4, 5, 6, 8, 10, 12, 15, 20, 24, 30, 40, 60 and 120 while 100 has only 1, 2, 4, 5, 10, 20, 50 and 100. Similarly, 10 has only four factors, 1, 2, 5 and 10, whereas 12 has 1, 2, 3, 4, 6 and 12 – half as many again – thus providing for easier mathematical calculation. Moreover, we have 12 months in the year, a 12-hour half day and 360 degrees in a circle as well as 12 in a dozen.

Notwithstanding such arguments, the notion that we might move to a duodecimal system by way of a replacement of our decimal system must be fanciful. It is notable, however, that several languages are reported to have used the system including Chepang (Nepal) and Mahl (India) as well as some Melanesian and Polynesian languages.

This observation highlights the fact that any particular number system is essentially language-based and serves to emphasise the central argument of this book that we must treat numbers and words as inextricably connected with each other rather than as indicating two separate disciplines.

13
NUMBER THIRTEEN

What an excuse!

A wealthy man – but a miser – received a visit from a delegation of three men representing a charity. "Of course I'll give you some money," he said deceitfully. "But first, each of you must write down a three-digit number of your choosing and repeat it."

The three men chose the following numbers:

A: 123,123   B: 876,876   C: 998,998

The wealthy man went on to say that he would pay to each of them the remainder arrived at by dividing their chosen number by 7, 11 or 13, again, as they themselves could choose.

A chose 7 as his divisor, **B** chose 11 and **C** chose 13. The three men got very excited. The odds of at least one of them coming away with a goodly sum seemed to them very high.

However, when **A** divided 123,123 by 7 he got 17,589 with a remainder equal to zero.

B divided 876,876 by 11 to get 79,716 remainder zero.

Finally, when **C** divided 998,998 by 13 he got 76,846 also with a zero remainder.

How could this happen? The three men became very upset.

So the wealthy man said he would be very fair and let each of them change his divisor. This time, **A** chose to divide by 13, **B** chose 7 and **C** chose 11. Nonetheless, they each got the same result – a remainder of zero.

They could not believe their bad luck having each been given the opportunity to select their own numbers. So they asked the wealthy man if they could try yet again with new divisors.

This time, **A** used 11, **B** used 13 and **C** used 7 but nevertheless the remainders in each case once again came to zero and the three men went away with nothing. They felt they had been very unlucky; that fate had dealt them and their good cause a severe blow.

However, this was not a matter of bad luck or of fate. It was a mathematical certainty demonstrating one of the interesting characteristics of numbers 7, 11 and 13.

Each of these divides exactly into any number which conforms to the pattern *abc,abc*, that is, without leaving a remainder. So 13, for example, is a factor of 613,613 as well as of 9,009 (which can be expressed as 009,009). As explained on page 63 this arises because any number following this pattern will be divisible exactly by 1,001 – and 1,001 results from multiplying the factors 7, 11 and 13 together.

Hence, any number of the construction *abc,abc* must be divisible by each of 7, 11 and 13. Try, for example, dividing 613,613 by 7, then the result by 11 and, in turn, the result of that by 13 and see what answer you get.

Some other characteristics of NUM13ER 13

In mathematics, 13 is a prime number, that is, a number having no factors other than itself and one.

It is also a Fibonacci number which is the subject of Chapter 26.

13 is the only integer which expressed to the powers of 1 and 4 in turn can be expressed as the sum of two consecutive squares. Hence:

$13^1 = 2^2 + 3^2$
$13^4 = 120^2 + 121^2$

1 divided by 13 (referred to as the reciprocal of 13) is a recurring or cyclic number, namely, 0.076923 076923 …

2 divided by 13 is even more interesting since it gives us 0.153846 153846… which is not only recurring but is a cyclic permutation of several other results of dividing by 13.

Hence:

5 divided by 13 gives 0.384615 384615...
6 divided by 13 gives 0.461538 461538...
7 divided by 13 gives 0.538461 538461...
8 divided by 13 gives 0.615384 615384...
11 divided by 13 gives 0.846153 846153...

In each case, the result comprises the same digits in a slightly different order.

Two other cyclic numbers are referred to on page 220, each having some interesting characteristics.

There are some unexpected tests for divisibility for the factor 13 as set out in Chapter 7.

Threotene

Whereas both the words *eleven* and *twelve* are derived from the idea of what is left over after subtracting 10, *thirteen* is a construct formed by the process of addition, that is, *thirteen* was originally the result of adding the two IE compounds *threo* and *tene* to create *threotene*.

Thirteen provides us with an example of metathesis (from the GK meaning "transposition"), a once commonly occurring process in language by which a sound in a word becomes transposed. Pronouncing the word *threotene* requires some effort and it is not hard to see how the transposition to *thirteen* would have occurred. The same process took place with the word *third*, derived from the OE *thridde*, whereas the letter R has retained its original position in the word *three*.

By a similar process, ME *drit* became *dirt*, OE *brinnan* became *burn*, and *girn* became *grin*. The original word *girn* still survives in the word *girning* – the practice of contorting the face muscles to produce grotesque faces.

Metathesis may be compared to Spoonerisms, so-called after W. A. Spooner (1844-1930) who produced much entertainment with transpositions such as "a well-boiled icicle" (instead of "a well-oiled bicycle") and "you have hissed my mystery lectures" (instead of "you have missed my history lectures").

Fear of thirteen

Thirteen, of course, is supposed to be unlucky – so much so that there is even a word for fear of the number, *triskaidekaphobia,* a Greek word first used as an English word in 1911.

So influenced are some of us by this ancient superstition that we apparently even take steps to avoid using the word *thirteen,* preferring phrases such as a baker's dozen or a long dozen.

14
SOME DIVERSIONS INVOLVING WORDS AND NUMBERS

Chess

Although mathematicians and chess players will share many of the same skills, including logical thought and pattern recognition, the game of chess as played by two players across a chessboard, as opposed to a chess match involving computers, is not inherently a mathematical game. One does not require mathematical prowess to be proficient at chess nor does the absence of mathematical skills indicate that one cannot be an accomplished chess player.

Nonetheless, there are many aspects of the game which require players to have basic numeracy skills. These include an ability to work with the numerical values assigned to each of the pieces, a facility at any stage of a game to work with the respective time that each player has left in order to make his remaining moves, and a facility to identify the address of each square on the chessboard so as to be able to record and recognise moves using standard chess notation which allocates a coordinate to each of the 64 squares in a grid from a1 to h8. In tournament play, where the participants play each other, grids may be required to keep tally of the scores and the ratings for the players are worked out with the aid of a mathematical formula.

Scrabble®

In Scrabble® the players take their turn to place letter tiles onto a board to make words. Each letter has a value and a tally is kept for each player of his score for each valid word placed on the board. That score will be increased if a letter tile played by any player falls on a square which is either a Double Letter or a Triple Letter square. His score will also be increased if his word falls on a Double Word square or a Triple Word square or consists of all seven tiles. The player with the highest score at the end of the game is the winner.

It can be seen that Scrabble® is a game which, in essence, involves converting letters into numbers. Letters and words are inextricably bound up with numbers in the game and it is said that, although Scrabble® is essentially a word game, prowess in the game depends more on mathematical or computational skills than on literacy. Indeed whilst players must be able to memorise lists of words, they need not have any understanding of the meanings of those words. However, to be able to play effectively, players have to be numerate.

Boggle®

The word game, Boggle®, employs a plastic box (with a lid) consisting of a grid of variously 4 x 4, 5 x 5 or 6 x 6 small square compartments accompanied by 16, 25 or 36 cubes according to the number of compartments. The cubes, each with letters of the alphabet printed on its six surfaces, are placed in the box and shaken up until each of those cubes falls into one of the compartments. Once the cubes slot into the grid in this way, the players have three minutes within which to identify and write down as many words of three letters or more which can be constructed from moving from any one cube to any adjacent cube. Some rules require a minimum of four-letter words.

The longer the word that is found, the greater the score for that word. In the 4 x 4 game of Boggle®, for example, the scoring is 1 point for a three- or four-letter word, 2 points for five letters, 3 for six letters, 5 for seven letters and 11 points for a word of eight or more letters. However, no player is entitled to score on a word unless he is the only player to have identified it.

Any number of players can participate, but two or three is the optimum. As might be expected, the winner is the player with the highest score.

This, then, is another game which involves converting words into numbers.

Bridge

The card game, bridge, played by four players, requires particular numerical dexterity in addition to the many other skills useful in a complex game of trick-winning where the best players will constantly be assessing which players have what cards and remember which cards have been played and by whom. Numeracy skills are required in bridge. You will need to:

- count the cards in your hand;
- reorder them so that they run in order of suit and value;
- calculate the aggregate point count of your hand by adding the appropriate points for each of your aces, court cards and voids;
- calculate how many tricks you might make if you become declarer;
- understand the bidding conventions and what they indicate as regards the cards held by the other three players;
- assess the odds of any opponent holding or not holding any particular card;
- assess the odds of any opponent holding a given number of cards in any suit;
- keep a tally of the tricks you have won and those you need to win in order to make your contract;
- calculate the score (either positive or negative) according to the number of tricks made;
- take into account the effect of a contract having been doubled or redoubled;
- work out the aggregate scores of the two teams (or of each player) at the end of the game.

In essence, bridge can be seen as a process whereby bids, expressed by the players in the first stage of the game, are translated into points.

Crossword puzzles

Crosswords, namely puzzles inviting solvers to fill in words horizontally and vertically in a pre-prepared grid by reference to given clues, come in many shapes and forms and varying degrees of complexity. Some puzzles might consist of simple word substitution tasks and, at the other end of the spectrum, others involve fiendishly intricate cryptic clues.

Crosswords were first published in the United States but gradually took on life in the United Kingdom in a more complex form – *The Times* having introduced its first cryptic puzzle on 1 February 1930.

It might seem that the whole substance of crosswords is made up of words and that the skill in completing them is purely lexical or linguistic. Numbers are involved in the process of solving puzzles only to a very limited extent, that is, in the numbering of the clues and in the quantification of the letters of each solution.

However, as regards the more difficult cryptic British-style crossword puzzle, that characterisation is confounded by recent research carried out by Drs. Kathryn Friedlander and Philip Fine of the University of Buckingham published in *Frontiers in Psychology* in May 2016. That study reveals that proficiency in completing such puzzles (particularly at speed) requires the kind of skills needed for code-breaking and solving quasi-algebraic problems and that most of the solvers surveyed had had training in mathematics or IT rather than in the arts. This is consistent with the fact that when in World War II Bletchley Park (the home of complex code-breaking) was seeking to recruit top candidates, it found that the best applicants were mathematicians rather than linguists.

Nim

The game of Nim is a mathematical game played by two players. It possibly originated in China and takes its current name from the German *nehmen*, meaning "to take", which in turn derives from the same Indo-European root *nem* from which the word *number* has developed.

Interest in Nim was invigorated by Alain Resnais's 1963 film *Last Year in Marienbad*.

The game comes in many forms but essentially involves setting out any number of objects (say, coins) arranged in any number of columns.

Let us use 15 coins set up as follows although there is no requirement to use any particular number of coins or any particular numbers of rows:

Rows

1	O
2	OO
3	OOO
4	OOOO
5	OOOOO

Fig.1

Players A and B take it in turns to take any number of coins from any **one** row with the objective of forcing the other to take the last coin on the table. The player who takes the last coin loses. In other variations the player who takes the last coin is the winner.

There is a system for winning based on the binary system which can be explained as follows:

1. Every position is either "safe" or "unsafe".

2. An unsafe position can, by any move, always be made into a safe one for the person making it.

3. Any move played in a safe position will render it unsafe for the person making it.

4. In determining whether a position is safe or unsafe, it is necessary to split the array of coins into quantities of 1s, 2s, 4s, 8s or 16s etc. (hence the binary connection). In working this out, we start with the largest possible binary quantity in any row and apply the same procedure to the balance of the coins left in any row so that a row of three coins will consist of one 2 and one 1.

5. To be safe, there must be an **even** number of each quantity in each set up, that is, an even number of 1s, 2s, 4s, 8s, 16s and so on.

6. In Fig.1, however, it can be seen that there are:

   Two sets of **4**s (rows 4 and row 5);
   Two sets of **2**s (rows 2 and 3); and
   Three sets of 1s (rows 1, 3 and 5).

In order to be safe, there must be an **even** number of each set or quantity so that the existence of **three** of the **1**s makes the position in Fig. 1 an unsafe position for Player A, the player who is to start.

7. To make it safe, Player A must therefore either remove the one coin in row 1 or one coin from row 3 or one coin from row 5. Any one of those three moves will produce a situation where there will be:

Two sets of **4**s;
Two sets of **2**s; and
Two sets of **1**s

– thus creating an **even** number of each set and hence an unsafe position for Player B.

8. The next turn by Player B (however many coins he might take from any row) must produce an unsafe position which player A can, on his turn, convert again into a position which is safe for him.

9. Eventually, the position must reduce to one where either:

a) there is only a single row left with more than one coin in it, in which event victory is obtained by the player whose turn it is to move by taking **all but one** of those coins; or

b) there are two rows of coins, one or more of which contains only one coin, in which event the game can be won by the player whose turn it is to move leaving intact the row with that one coin in it and **taking all the coins in the other row**.

This is because, in either case, the next player to move will have no choice but to take the last coin, thus losing the game.

There are many websites on which you can play "against the computer" in order to practise but here is something to get your teeth into. Applying the above rules, which coin or coins should you remove in the following position in Fig. 2 to keep the position safe? **Question S.**

Rows

1	O
2	OO
3	OO
4	OOO
5	OOOOO

Fig. 2

The answer to **Question S** is on page 214.

Nimword

A variation of Nim, called Nimword, is played as a word game. Best played by two players, they each select any 15-letter English word. Anagram dictionaries are a convenient source for these. Each player copies his own word onto a sheet of paper and has just three minutes to carry out the following task, working simultaneously without reference to each other.

Players start by deleting one or more letters of their choosing from the original 15-letter word and try to make a new dictionary word (but only one) from the remaining letters, whether by way of anagram play or by leaving intact an internal string of letters in the original word.

Once a player has constructed his first new word in this way, he repeats the exercise by taking away a further letter or letters from the new word and remodels the letters remaining to form another new dictionary word. And so on until only two letters remain.

After the first three minutes, the players swap their original 15-letter words and carry out the same exercise.

The winner is the player who, over both rounds, has created the greater number of new words having two or more letters.

By way of example, two players select the following two words from which, on the first round, they come up with the following new words:

ROUND ONE

DISENTANGLEMENT	and	MISREPRESENTING
Player A		Player B

Player A	Player B
Deletes DI and makes ENTANGLEMENTS	Deletes ING making MISREPRESENT
Deletes S making ENTANGLEMENT	Deletes MI making REPRESENTS
Deletes MENT making ENTANGLE	Deletes S making PRESENTER
Deletes N making ELEGANT	Deletes ER making PRESENT
Deletes L making NEGATE	Deletes P making RESENT
Deletes NE making GATE	Deletes N making STEER
Deletes E making TAG	Deletes E making REST
Deletes G making TA	Deletes R making SET
	Deletes S making TE

ROUND TWO

They then swap words and carry out a similar exercise:

MISREPRESENTING	and	DISENTANGLEMENT
Player A		Player B

Player A	Player B
Deletes MIS making REPRESENTING	Deletes MENT making DISENTANGLE
Deletes RE making PRESENTING	Deletes DI making ENTANGLES
Deletes R making RESENTING	Deletes S making ENTANGLE
Deletes S making ENTERING	Deletes EN making TANGLE
Deletes N making INTEGER	Deletes T making ANGLE
Deletes G making ENTIRE	Deletes E making LANG
Deletes E making INERT	Deletes L making NAG
Deletes R making TINE	Deletes G making AN
Deletes I making TEN	
Deletes T making EN	

The aggregate score for Player B is 17 words whereas Player A scores 18 and wins.

15
NON-SPECIFIC NUMBERS

Empty numbers

Empty numbers are numbers used in colloquial speech but which do not appear in dictionaries of mathematics. They can be expressed in words but cannot be expressed in figures. Numbers of this kind are sometimes described as "non-specific", "indefinite" or "empty" numbers. Included in this category are nouns such as *umpteen* and *zillion*.

There are many such words and phrases consisting of nouns and adjectives (referred to as "quantifiers") which are used to indicate uncertainty as to a particular quantity or to express emphasis.

We use terms such as *the whole, all, every, plenty, many, some, several* (and *severalth), lots of, stacks of, tons of* and *heaps of* when there is an inability or a reluctance to be specific. Likewise, the phrase *a great deal* is a convenient but lazy way of referring to an indeterminate amount. It could also refer to a large tree, an excellent bargain or a good hand of cards. *N number of...* and *any number of...* indicate an indeterminate number as does the word *countless*. Similarly, we use phrases such as *the remainder, the rest, the balance* and *what is left over*.

We sometimes use the adverb *betimes* meaning "on occasions or sometimes". The slang term *yonks* (or *for yonks*) indicates a long indeterminate period.

The prefix *pluri-* indicates several in number. The OED indicates more than 40 words so prefixed including the ugly but useful word *plurisignation* (sometimes *plurisignification*) used mainly in literary criticism to indicate a term, a passage or even a whole work which has various layers of meaning or ambiguity. And there is the plurisignative word *plurality* which, Janus-like, means more than one whilst reserving the possibility of an infinite number. The prefix *pluri-* has its origins in the IE *pel* or *ple*, meaning "full", from which we get a plethora of words such as *plethora* (an over-abundance), *plenary* (complete as in a plenary session), *plebs* (the populace) and the many words beginning with *poly-* such as *polygamy* (the state of having many spouses), *polychromatic* (many-coloured) and *polytechnic* (skilled in many disciplines).

Expressions such as *tens, scores, hundreds* and *thousands* when applied to an unknown quantity of things provide us with a paradox in that whereas each of those words constitutes, in mathematics, a clear finite term, when used colloquially that clarity evaporates and metamorphoses into a vague cloud.

To indicate uncertainty of a greater order, we can turn to words such as *umpteen* (sometimes *umteen*) meaning a large indeterminate number. The word originates from World War I when it was used by signallers to avoid disclosing specific numbers of troop movements. Eric Partridge suggested that the *um-* may derive from the non-committal sound we use in everyday speech. That conjures up a vivid picture of a stressed officer hurriedly composing a message but hesitating before specifying a precise number of soldiers and deciding, instead, to combine his expression of that hesitancy by using the suffix *-teen* and, in the process, coining a new term.

Umpteen, umteenth and *umpty* are suggestive of a number under a hundred. To indicate a much greater order of uncertainty, a different device is required such as the slang *zillion* and *squillion* indicating a very large but indeterminate number having an obvious reference to a *million* or a *billion*. In the United States words such as *bazillion, gazillion, squillion* and *jillion* have been coined. None of those four terms indicates anything other than a non-specific large number.

Another term is available to express this notion, namely *myriad* from the Greek *murias Mu* (M) representing ten thousand. In Archimedes' time, numbers were expressed as names and there were no names for numbers in excess of ten thousand. *Myriad* is rarely used today in that sense. It is used now more as an adjective to indicate "countless" or "innumerable" and also as a plural noun with the same connotation.

-ness

When confronted with a small number of objects or things how do we determine how many there are? If we are playing on a "one-armed bandit" or gaming machine we know instantly how many cherries there are in the winning line. We do not need to count them. Similarly, when playing with dice, we need not count the spots; we immediately recognise the pattern and do not need to count them up.

There is a term used in psychology to describe this innate facility – the verb *to subitise* (from the L *subitus*, sudden) meaning "to discern without counting the number of items in a small sample". Most of us can subitise up to six items. For greater numbers, we must resort to the more ponderous chore of having to count although, with practice, it is possible, by recognising patterns, to subitise larger quantities. The numbers one to six can thus be seen to have a special quality.

There is a linguistic device for generating words which express a state or condition of this kind. This consists of adding the suffix *-ness* to adjectives, participles or numbers. Hence, we find the word *oneness* indicating the quality of being single or one in number. The OED also contains *onceness* (the quality of occurring once only) and *firstness* (the quality of being first). *Twoness* (the quality or state of being two) is found in the OED as is *secondness* (the quality of being second). The words *thirdness* and *threeness* also appear but not *fourness*, *fiveness* or higher values (although some do occur in other dictionaries). Perhaps the absence of any need for such words is conditioned by our inability to subitise larger numbers.

The OED also contains the word *ninetyishness* referring to characteristics redolent of the 1890s.

Pluralising nouns

The method of showing a non-specific quantity of anything, as a matter of syntax, is simply to pluralise the noun in question.

How do we pluralise nouns? Well, that is easy; we simply add an *-s* to the end of the word. *Noun – nouns*. There are obviously some exceptions to this general rule but we might underestimate just how many of these exceptions there are.

To pluralise nouns we add an *-s* at the end of the word:

Except with some words ending in *s, ch, sh, x* or *z* such as *stress, brush, march, minx* and *klutz* when we add an *-es.*

Except in the case of *wife, knife* and *life* – the plurals of which end in *-ives* (although not when we refer to *still lifes*).

And **except** with words ending in *y,* such as *quantity,* the plural of which requires an *-ies* ending (although the plurals of *buoy* and *boy* do involve adding an *-s* and the plural of *passerby* is *passersby*).

And **except** with the plurals of *tooth, foot, louse* and *goose,* namely, *teeth, feet, lice* and *geese* (although the plural of *mongoose* is *mongooses*). The plural of *house* is *houses* but of *mouse* it is *mice.*

And **except** for *calf, half* and *wolf* – the plurals of which are *calves, halves* and *wolves.*

And **except** for the plurals of words such as *man* (plural *men* although the plural of *talisman* is *talismans*) and *woman* (which incidentally is the only word the plural of which, *women*, involves a different pronunciation for both syllables when compared with the singular). Then we have *child – children, brother – brethren* and *ox – oxen* (although the plural of *fox* is *foxes*).

And **except** for one particular word which is pluralised by inserting a letter one before the end – *die* plural *dice.*

And **except** for the amazing rhinoceros, the only word with four plurals: *rhinoceroses, rhinoceri, rhinocerotes* and *rhinoceros.*

Except for *cow* and the pronoun *I,* the plurals of which (*kine* and *we*) contain none of the letters which are comprised in their singular forms.

Except for *beau,* the plural of which is *beaux,* although *beau geste* bucks the trend requiring both an *x* and an *s* to form its plural *beaux gestes.* The plural of *bureau* is *bureaus* although the plural of *bureau de change* is *bureaux de change.* Both of these phrases – *beaux gestes* and *bureaux de change* – when pluralised are pronounced in exactly the same way as they are in their singular form. Words such as *précis, corps, rendezvous, chassis* and *faux pas* have the same spellings in their singular form as they do in their plural and yet the singular and plural of each is pronounced differently.

Except for many words of Greek origin which, when pluralised, have other habits such as *analysis/analyses* and *crisis/crises* – a one-letter change but not the last letter. The plurals of *criterion* and *phenomenon* are created by substituting the one letter -*a* for the last two letters.

And **except** for some words with a Latin etymology which also have their own rules such as *stratum* becoming *strata*, *radius/radii* and *cactus/cacti* although *radiuses* and *cactuses* appear in some dictionaries. The plural of *corpus* is *corpora*. The plural of *formula* is *formulae* and the plural of *index* is created by deleting the last two letters and substituting four different ones to produce *indices*. The plural of *podium* can be either *podia* or *podiums* but the plural of *medium* is *media* unless one is referring to those communicating with the next world when the plural is *mediums*.

And **except** for some words ending with an -*o* such as *tomato*, *cargo* and *echo* – the plurals of which are respectively *tomatoes*, *cargoes* and *echoes* whereas the plurals of *ghetto* and *dynamo* are *ghettos* and *dynamos*. *Zero*, the noun, has two possible plurals – *zeros* (preferred by Fowler) and *zeroes* (OED). However, when used as a verb (as in, *to zero in*), the plural is *zeroes*. When used as an adjective, *zero* is unusual; by definition, it can have no plural and yet it often takes a plural noun as in *zero degrees*. *Duo* also has two plurals – *duos* and the odd -looking *dui*.

And **except** for *basis* and *oasis* which already have their concluding -*s* and whose plurals are *bases* and *oases*.

And **except** for *cherub* and *seraph*, the plurals of which are *cherubim* and *seraphim*.

And **except** for compound nouns such as *son-in-law*, the plural of which (if you are lucky enough) is *sons-in-law*, but if you celebrate and have more than one *gin and tonic* you drink *gin and tonics* rather than *gins and tonics*.

Currency and coins also seem to create confusion. The plural of *penny* depends on whether you are referring to coins (*pennies*) or to a sum of money (*pence*). Few words have given rise to as much uncertainty as *euro* when it comes to determining the plural form. This is partly because the correct plural form differs according to the language in which the term is being used so that the

French should refer to *100 euros* while the prescribed form in Germany is *100 euro*. Furthermore, as regards the UK, while in EU legislation and legal texts the required plural is *euro*, it is acceptable in everyday English usage to use the plural *euros* which more closely follows the rules of English grammar. The notion, therefore, that it is incorrect to refer to *euros* is wrong as the European Commission Directorate-General for Translation's *English Style Guide* makes clear.

Curiously, while we thus often use the plural *euros*, we frequently refer, colloquially, to *pounds* in the singular such as in "it cost five pound fifty".

Million can optionally take an *s* in a sentence which has no noun head so "there were several million" or "there were several millions".

Nouns such as *dozen* and *hundred* are not pluralised if they are preceded by another quantitative word (five hundred runners) but they will be when followed by the word *of* (hundreds of runners). We say *three score and ten* but *scores of people*.

And **except** for nouns such as *amends* (as in "to make amends"), *riches, goods, scissors, trousers, jeans, pyjamas, clothes, Antipodes* and *smithereens* – none of which appear to have a singular form although they each end with an *s*; nor do nouns such as *bedclothes, elevenses, sea-legs, outskirts, headquarters* or *The Outer Hebrides*. Nor does *paraphernalia* have a singular form.

In contrast, some words such as *people, offspring, role-play* and *horsepower* do not appear to have a plural form. Nouns such as *knowledge, propaganda, compassion* and *thunder* do not appear to have a singular or a plural. They are a kind of "hermaphrodite" noun.

There are many other apparent plural nouns each ending with the letter *-s* such as *innings, mews* and *news* – "Here is the news" – and the names of games such as *darts, billiards* and *draughts* which are treated as singular nouns. Although ending in an *-s*, nouns such as *mathematics* and *linguistics* are also treated as singular. We have also been conditioned to accept as normal the daily revelation that "Windows™ is shutting down".

Then there are words which are pluralised twice. This occurs where nouns have been imported into the English language from the plural form such as *opera* (singular L *opus*) and *agenda* (singular L *agendum*) but in the plural become *operas* and *agendas*. *Data* (the plural of L *datum*) and *graffiti* (the plural of L *graffito*) are used both as singular nouns and plural nouns. *Trivia* takes both a singular and plural verb.

The colloquialism, *lots of*, appears to indicate the plural yet it takes a singular verb **except**, that is, when used with a plural noun so that we say "there **is** lots to do" but "there **are** lots of things to do".

And **except** for nouns such as *sheep, deer, moose, cod, salmon, wheat, series* and *means* (in the sense of a method) which retain the same form whether used in the singular or the plural.

There is nothing particularly unusual about the plural of *miss* (the feminine title) except that when that plural (*misses*) is pronounced it sounds as if the marital status of the subject has changed.

And after we learn all these exceptions and vagaries we are thrown back into disarray when we meet plural verbs such as "Thomas **mans** the pumps", "Michael **foots** the bill" and "Virginia **wolfs** her dinner down".

These vagaries even extend to the pronunciation of the humble letter -*s* which has three different phonetic manifestations. In words such as *prizes, causes* and *lunches* it is pronounced as (ᵊz). In words such as *eggs* the -*s* is pronounced as if it were a (z) whereas in their complement, *chips,* it is pronounced as a simple (*s*).

Perhaps pluralising nouns in the English language is not that simple.

16
NUMBERS AND WORDS IN DISGUISE

Numbers in disguise

Is the word *eight* a number as well as a word? We should characterise *eight* as a word which indicates a number. Here the number indicated is obvious. However, there are many words or phrases which indicate numbers in a non-obvious way and these are referred to as "numbers in disguise".

We find numbers hidden in words such as *fortnight* which is short for fourteen nights. The related *sennight,* short for and meaning "a period of seven nights", is now rarely used where the OE word *week* is more than adequate for the job and now has an overwhelming monopoly.

Whether for comic effect or to introduce some variation to the monotony involved in reeling out a series of numbers, bingo callers customarily employ colourful terms for the numbers they are calling, for example "Kelly's eye" for number one (according to Eric Partridge this may be an anecdotal reference to a one-eyed Kelly) and "two fat ladies", a now politically incorrect reference to the number 88.

Bingo callers also use rhyming slang such as:

Buttered bun	signifying	1
Knock on the door		4
Man alive		5
Pick up sticks		6
Gates of heaven		7

Garden gate	8
Mother of mine	9
Uncle Ben	10
Dinky doo	22
Clickety-click	66

Slang dictionaries provide a plentiful supply of numbers in disguise. Slang serves many functions. It is used as a secret language, a means of seeking superiority over the uninitiated, a diversion from the norm, a bonding mechanism, a euphemism, a humorous means of communicating or merely as a shorthand. The following examples of Cockney slang serve as convenient abbreviations for money sums:

Carpet	£3, £30 or £300 or, in betting, the odds 3 to 1 ("carpet bag" was rhyming slang for "drag", a three-month prison sentence)
Bluey	£5 (in reference to the note being blue in colour)
Deep sea diver	£5 or *fiver* (rhyming slang)
Tony Benn	£10 (rhyming slang)
Pony	£25 (of uncertain origin but perhaps from the pony once depicted on a 25-rupee banknote)
Macaroni	£25 (rhyming slang for *pony*)
Monkey	£500 (of unknown origin)
Bag of sand (or merely **Bag**)	£1,000 (rhyming slang for *grand* – a US term for $1,000)
Archer	£2,000 (being the amount apparently paid by Jeffrey Archer to Monica Coghlan to leave the UK)

Numbers connoting words and phrases

The slang examples above are instances where the slang consists of words used to express numbers. Rhyming slang also employs numbers in the form of words to represent non-mathematical matters such as in the following examples:

Baker's dozen	a cousin
Eighteen pence	sense
Forty-four	a door-to-door salesman
Two-thirty	dirty
To half-inch	to steal or "pinch"
Half-an-hour	flour
Twos and threes	keys
Ones and twos	shoes
To be at sixes and sevens	to be in a state of disorder or confusion
To be in a two and eight (or six and eight)	to be in an emotional state or panic

Some numbers, by dint of frequent use, serve as a shorthand or a kind of "trademark" for the ideas or for things they originally represented such as:

24/7	throughout the day and night
18	a film in the UK with an 18 certificate indicating suitability only for those of 18 years or over
45 and 78	vinyl records playing on both sides at 45 or 78 revs per minute
4 by 4	a four-wheel drive vehicle
9 to 5	office hours and, by extension, a boring routine as in the song of the same name written and performed by Dolly Parton
5 to 7	an assignation, as in Victor Levin's 2015 film of the same name about a New York romance
1984	the title of George Orwell's 1949 novel referring to a totalitarian society which employs overarching surveillance
20/20	perfect vision or, more correctly, the ability to see without wearing glasses to an accuracy of a normal person

Many number words and phrases serve as a shorthand such as *ten-four* ("message received and understood" – one of the many abbreviations in the so-called US ten-codes originally used on the radio by the police and other emergency services), *two-one (2:1)* and *two-two (2:2)* (referring to the two levels of a second-class degree awarded by UK universities) and *one over the eight* (originally military slang for being drunk where eight pints of beer was the set limit).

Amongst the many other number words which have developed a non-number significance are *foursquare* which is used both as an adverb meaning "firmly" and as an adjective meaning "firm or not yielding", *two-timer* meaning "someone who is unfaithful", *two-faced* meaning "deceitful", *third party* which, in insurance, refers to anyone other than the insured and *sixth sense* meaning "a special power of perception".

Back slang

Back slang provides another example of numbers in disguise. It is a means of communicating in "code" by substituting for any word its reverse, that is to say, by reversing the letters of a particular word and pronouncing the result with or without the interpolation of additional letters or some other change made necessary to aid pronunciation. Hence, *kacab genals* is back slang for *back slang*. There are many other variations of so-called back slang used by children, involving the interposing of two letters (for example A and G) before each vowel sound so that the number 27 would be pronounced "twagentagy sagevagen".

Back slang employs word reversal and was probably created in Victorian England by costermongers and hawkers, market traders and butchers to allow traders who are working together to communicate without their customers appreciating precisely what is being said – particularly about the cost of their wares. One of the first references to this species of slang was in Henry Mayhew's *London Labour and the London Poor* in 1851. Here are some examples:

Eno	one
Owt	two
Eerht, earth or *erth*	three
Rouf or *roaf*	four
Evif	five

Xis, exis or exxes	six
Neves or nevis	seven
Eenin	nine
Net	ten
Nevele	eleven
Evlenet	twelve

Slang is still used in betting to avoid punters becoming aware of changing odds. In addition, bookies at some greyhound and horse race tracks still use tic-tac involving frenzied hand signals and the whole range of rhyming and back slang to indicate current odds.

Letters in disguise

By employing a mechanical operation or an algorithm, ciphers are used both in times of peace and war to encrypt text in order to conceal the original message so as to maintain confidentiality or secrecy.

Some ciphers achieve this by converting each of the letters of the words of the message into numbers. Before the advent of computers, the most basic cipher might simply use the device of allocating to each letter of the alphabet a discrete number generated by taking the place that that letter holds in the alphabet whether in its unadulterated form or after it had been manipulated.

Such manipulation might, for example, be effected by prefacing, say, the Roman alphabet with a pre-selected keyword which has no duplicate letters and by avoiding the duplication of any letter in the remainder of the alphabet. Hence, if the keyword "cipher" were to be agreed between the sender and intended recipient of the message for this purpose, the key would be:

c	i	p	h	e	r	a	b	d	f	g	j	k	l	m	n	o	q	s	t	u	v	w	x	y	z
1	2	3	4	5	6	7	8	9	10	11	12	13	14	15	16	17	18	19	20	21	22	23	24	25	26

– where each letter of the alphabet occurs once only.

Using the above keyword would produce the string 1-17-9-5 to indicate the word CODE.

Further security might be achieved by reversing the alphabet or using some other pre-agreed device although an experienced cryptanalyst would have no problem in deciphering this form of code.

Valuing letters

Although ciphers of this kind play no part in modern cryptography, they do present us with an amusing endeavour. Let us simply give each of the letters A to Z a number corresponding to its position in the alphabet thus:

a	b	c	d	e	f	g	h	i	j	k	l	m	n	o	p	q	r	s	t	u	v	w	x	y	z
1	2	3	4	5	6	7	8	9	10	11	12	13	14	15	16	17	18	19	20	21	22	23	24	25	26

A task we might then set ourselves, in competition, is to identify any word (found, say, in *The Chambers Dictionary* and having more than three letters) which produces the highest score. This is ascertained by working out the aggregate score for the word as a whole and dividing that score by the number of letters in the word. Hence, RECORDS with seven letters will give an aggregate score of 82 and an average score of 11.7 (being $82/7$).

However, of course, RECORDS can easily be broken. Playing PUZZLER, for example, would produce a score of 17.7 and there are many words which will produce higher scores. When you have exhausted using the alphabet, A to Z, you could try with a more complex system for valuing the letters of the alphabet so that this game has infinite dimensions, especially when accompanied by a computer program which can automatically calculate the results.

Counting-out games

In playing games (such as or Tag or Tig) children all over the world are familiar with counting-out procedures of many different kinds by which they can decide which of them in the group is to be excluded from the game they are playing or is to be selected to take on a particular role in it – that child often being referred to as "it". In a typical procedure, children stand in a line or in a circle and one of them, the "counter", counts out his fellow playmates one by one in a process called "dipping" until only one of them remains and becomes "it". The counting process often consists of the counter chanting the words of a rhyme or a piece of doggerel (often gibberish) and pointing to his playmates in turn as he comes to each word so that, for example, the seventh child in line would become "it" in a rhyme such as:

Olicka bolicka
Susan solicka
Olicka bolicka
Nob.   (Iona & Peter Opie, *Children's Games In Street & Playground*; OUP, 1969)

In effect, each word serves as a number. In some cases, the words of the doggerel may actually derive from numbers. For example, in the doggerel "Hickory, Dickory Dock" (now better known as the beginning of a well-known nursery rhyme), the first three words are thought to represent the numbers eight, nine and ten. Similarly with other nonsense verses (and their very many variations) such as the following sets of first lines:

- Yan, Tan, Tethera, Methera;
- Een, Teen, Peever, Pepperer;
- Ip, Dip, Alaba Da; and the well-known
- Eeny, Meeny, Miny, Mo.

In each of these, the words possibly constitute the process of counting one, two, three, four. Some such verses, it is thought, may originate from an obscure Cumbrian or Celtic dialect or some long-lost British counting system of the past. It is, perhaps, the fascination which young children have with the unknown or mystical which accounts for the lasting appeal of such games.

There are many hundreds of such similar verses recorded in the English-speaking world as well as on the continent of Europe. Their origins are, at present, largely a matter of conjecture. Each has many variations and none has a definitive version, which may be explained by the delight children take in improvisation and the fact that such rhymes spread, from playground to playground, merely by word of mouth.

Whatever the origins of these widespread and enduring diversions, they demonstrate a deep-rooted and visceral connection between language and numbers.

17
ORIGINS AND CATEGORIES OF NUMBER WORDS

Some origins

Our lives are often given additional depth of meaning by a family tree. Our heritage helps to position us and to enable us to come to terms with our identity. Sometimes, knowledge of our ancestry might supply insights and explanations into that identity in a way which is totally unexpected but which, when revealed to us, can make such good sense that we wonder why we had never previously "seen the light".

Studying the origins or the roots of words can likewise provide revealing insights. This chapter concentrates on those words not already referred to in Chapter 6 whose heritage can be found in the numbers one to ten. In many of the following examples, unpicking the word origin presents us with an unexpected yet insightful explanation.

ONE (from the IE *oino*) provides us with a host of words beginning with *uni-* such as *unity, unit, unique* and *unify*. *Unison,* (from the Latin *uni-* and *sonus*) means "one sound" and *unanimous* (*unus* and *animus*) indicates "of one mind". *Universe* refers to the whole world from where we get *university*, meaning "the entire community of teachers and students". From *one* we also get *once* and words such as *alone, lone, lonely, only* (*one* plus *–ly*), *anon* (in one moment) and perhaps also *onion* (successive layers creating a unity). The word *none* is short for "not one" and *atone* is merely a shortened form of "being at one", whence *atonement*. From *oino* we derive *ounce* and also *inch* so that the same root is the origin of both one of the smallest of measures and, in *universe*, one of the largest. The Greek prefix *mono-*, meaning "one" or "a singularity", gives us a multitude of words including *monotheism, monopoly, monotony* and *monoxide.*

There are many words which are descended from the roots of the word **TWO,** namely, IE *duo/dwo,* GK *di-* and L *bi-*. We start with obvious examples such as *duologue, duplicate, duplicity, double, doubloon* (a Spanish gold coin worth two pistols), *duo, duet, dual* and *duel* (a fight between two persons). *Deuce* refers to a two in cards, dominoes or dice. Less obvious derivatives are *between* (surrounded by two others), *dubious* (of two minds) and *doubt,* both from the L *dubitare* meaning "to waver". *Two* is cognate with *twice, twin, twelve, twig* (dividing into two) and *twine* (made of two threads), hence *entwine* and *twist*. This is how we also get the word *twain* (signifying two as in the phrase "ne'er the twain shall meet"). *Twilight* (half-light) is yet another beneficiary of the connection with *two. Two* is also cognate with *twenty* although we use the Greek *icos-* to generate *icosian* and the Latin *vicenari-* to give us *vicenary,* both of which mean "pertaining to twenty".

There is a plethora of words commencing with *bi-* as in *biplane, bilateral* and *bigamy*. Less obvious examples of the influence of the root come in words such as *biscuit* (from the French, twice-cooked) and *combine* (to join two things). The word *binary* (pertaining to two) has a special significance in mathematics and gave birth to the ubiquitous *bit* (formed by abbreviating *binary digit*).

Biennial (as well as *bi-weekly* and *bi-monthly*) often causes confusion. In reference to plants, *biennial* means those which have a two-year lifecycle although generally it means occurring once every two years. *Biennial* is sometimes used instead of its lookalike, *biannual,* which means occurring half-yearly or twice in the course of a year. Because of the ambiguity of these words, it is better to avoid them or to supplement them with words making the intention clear.

From *di-* we derive *dichotomy* (a division into two parts or a paradox) and *dilemma* which is referred to in Chapter 6.

The IE root of **THREE** is *tre-* or *tri-* and the Latin root *tertius,* from which we derive words such as *three, thrice, trio, third, trilogy, triplet, tripod, treble, thrice, triangle* and *tertiary* (third ranking). A few of the less obvious connections with these roots are the words *trellis* (three-threaded), *tribe* (referring originally to one of the three divisions of the inhabitants of Rome) and hence *tribunal* (someone chosen to represent a tribe).

From *tertius* (more specifically the Latin *nudius tertius* meaning "today is the third day") we derive the adjective *nudiustertian* relating to the day before yesterday.

The name *Ridings* in the North, West and East Ridings of Yorkshire was originally *Thriding* (indicating the existence of three districts), the initial *th* becoming obscured in the *th* of North.

The roots of **FOUR** are IE *kuetuer*, the Greek *tetrad* and the Latin *quadrant*. *Tetra-* provides us with the prefix of a host of words from *tetrathlon* (a sporting contest involving four events) to *tetragram* (a more elegant way of referring to a word with four letters) and the swanky *tetraglot* (a person speaking four languages).

The farthing, which was legal tender in the UK until the end of 1960, derives from *fourthling* or a fourth part.

We derive even more words from the root *quad* including *quadrant*, *quadrangle*, *quadratic*, *quarter*, *quatrain* and *quartet*. Less obvious descendants are *square* (having four sides), *squad* and *squadron* (an array of soldiers in a square formation). We also derive the words *quire* (in mediaeval times, four sheets of paper), *quadrennium* or *quadriennium* (a period of four years) and *quarantine* (a period of isolation originally lasting about 40 days).

FIVE arrives from IE *penkue* and L *quintus*. The *Punjab* derives its name in reference to its five rivers. *Pentecost* is celebrated as a Christian festival on the Sunday 50 days after Easter. Three less obvious derivations are the words *punch* (a drink made from five ingredients), *finger* (five on each hand) and *fist* which is cognate with *finger*.

There are, of course, many words with the prefix *penta-*. The OED contains around 30 main entries for such words including *pentagon*, *pentangle*, *pentagram*, *Pentateuch* and *pentathlon*.

From *quintus* we derive another group of words including the obvious *quintet* and *quintuplets* and the less obvious *quintessential* (see page 50).

SIX comes to us from IE *seks*, GK *hex* and L *sex*. Hence, we have words such as *sextant* (an instrument having an arc of a sixth part of a circle), *sextuplets* (six children born together) and *hexagon* (a six-sided figure). Other words derived from this root are *semester* (originally a period lasting six months), *siesta* (a rest taken six hours after sunrise), referred to on page 76, and *senary* (pertaining to the number six).

IE *Septm*, L *Septem* and GK *hepta* each indicate the number **SEVEN** from which words such as *September* (originally the seventh month) and *septuagenarian* (someone in their seventies) derive. We also get *heptagon* (a seven-sided figure) and *hebdomadal* (meeting or taking place once a week).

EIGHT derives from IE *okto*, L *octo* and GK *okta* from whence we get words such as *octet, octagonal, octopus, octogenarian* and *octane* (having eight carbon atoms) as well as *October* (originally the eighth month).

NINE has the roots IE *neun*, L *novem* and GK *ennead* which give us words such as *November* (originally the ninth month) and *noon* (the ninth hour after sunrise as the Romans saw it; see page 75). *Ennead* is used to mean a set of nine things or nine people.

From the number **TEN** and its roots IE *dekm*, L *decem* and GK *deka* we derive words such as *twenty, teens, tithe* (originally the tenth part of a person's agricultural produce paid by way of tax) and *dime* (10 cents). Both a *doyen* (originally a leader of ten) and *dean* (in Roman times the commander of a division of ten soldiers) are closely related. We also derive *dozen* from the L *duodecim* meaning "two plus ten". Then there are the more obvious derivatives such as *decade, decimal, decibel* (one tenth of a Bell being the unit of sound named after Alexander Graham Bell) and *December* (originally the tenth month; see page 51). *Decimate* originally meant to reduce by one tenth although it has now come, less exactly, to mean the destruction of a large proportion. *Decuple* means "tenfold" or "ten times as much", constructed in the same way as *double, triple* and *quadruple*.

Cardinal numbers

The above ten numbers together with zero and all following whole numbers or integers are described as cardinal numbers.

The word *cardinal* has a variety of meanings all derived from the L *cardo*, meaning "hinge" and, by extension, anything of fundamental importance on which something else revolves. Hence, the use of the word *cardinal* to describe the highest-ranking officials of the Roman Catholic Church after the Pope;

the colour *cardinal* or *cardinal red* to describe the colour of their vestments; *cardinal point,* one of the four principal points of the horizon; and *cardinal sins* in Christian theology, those sins considered to be the most serious human transgressions.

To the question "How many athletes ran the London marathon this year?" the answer will be a cardinal number. Cardinal numbers are also used in the process of counting one, two, three etc. and are used as a pronominal ("there are six in a box") and also as an adjective ("I have read 136 pages").

Cardinal numbers are to be contrasted with the following categories of numbers which, in turn, answer different questions.

Ordinal adjectives

To the question "Where did you come in the race?" the answer would be expressed as an ordinal number. Hence, *first, second, third, fourth,* etc. are ordinals describing position or order in any particular series. *Zeroth* is also used principally in physics.

There is a close relationship between each of the cardinals and their respective ordinals except in the cases of *first, second* and *third* where we might have expected *onth, twoth* and *threeth* consistent with the basic model of adding the letters *th* to each cardinal to create the corresponding ordinal.

First comes via the IE *per,* adapted in Germanic, to give other cognate words such as *before, former* and *foremost.*

Second originates from IE *seku,* to follow, which gives us cognate words such as *sect* (those following a common philosophy), *non sequitur* (something which does not logically follow), *persecute, obsequious* (describing someone who follows compliantly), *sign* (a mark which is to be followed) and a host of other associated words including *sequel.* The OED also contains *threequel* being the third in a sequence of films.

The derivation of *third* is referred to on page 107.

Ordinal adverbs

Ordinal adverbs are words constituting a separate category of enumeration in the form of adverbs. They follow closely the form of ordinal adjectives but with the addition of the suffix *-ly*. Like ordinal adjectives, they express the order in a set rather than any quantity, hence *firstly, secondly, thirdly, fourthly*, etc.

Ranking numbers

To the question "What degree of importance do you give to athletics in your life?" the answer may be a *primary, secondary* or *tertiary* importance. There are terms of ranking which extend to higher degrees but they are rarely used.

Multiplicative numeration

"How often have you run a London Marathon?" The answer to this question would be one of the multiplicative numbers in column 7 in Fig. 2 below – provided that you have not run more than three marathons. This is because there are only three such multiplicatives, namely, *once, twice* and *thrice*. If you have run four marathons, the answer would have to be in the form of "four times" and so on. Given our ready predisposition to create new words, it is odd that no discrete adverbs have been coined beyond once, twice, and thrice. Perhaps the reason for this omission is connected with our ability to subitise up to only six objects (see page 119) although that does not explain why we do not have words such as *fource, fice* and *sice* to indicate four, five or six times.

In the phrase "in (at) a trice" (instantly), the word *trice* has no connection with *thrice* as one might have expected. *Trice* here relates to the verb *trice* meaning "to pull or pluck", referring to sudden force.

Replicative numbers

The question "What kinds of marathon have you run?" might generate a replicative answer such as "a single and a double marathon".

The word *single* originates from the IE *sem*, meaning "one", "the same" or "together" from which we derive many words including *simultaneous, similar, simile* and *assimilate*. *Double* comes from the IE root *duo* referred to above in connection with *two*. Its use here is most interesting in that in the Middle Ages (and for some time after) the word *other* signified "second", a usage which remains with us today in phrases such as "on the other hand", "every other day", "the other day" and "the other woman". In Swedish, the second floor of a building is called the *andra våningen*, literally "the other floor". Although words such as *both, either* and *rather* are not cognate it is remarkable that (as with *neither*) they each contain the two letters *th* and that each of them has a close resonance with the notion of a choice between two subject matters or alternatives.

Those words indicating a multiple or a group and which end in *-plex, -ple* or *-plicate* (such as *duplex, triple* and *triplicate*) look back to the IE *pel* or *plek* meaning "to fold or bend" from which we also derive words such as *plait, pliant, pliable, pleat, plywood, ply* and *reply* (the reply being the original folded letter which was used for the response).

Names of polygons

Our numbers, from three onwards, are used in describing different kinds of polygon.

The noun *polygon* derives from the GK *poly-, polus* meaning "many", which is used in a large number of words including *polytechnic* (many arts), *Polynesia* (many islands) and *polymer* (the bonding of many units). The other syllable of *polygon* is from the GK *gonia* meaning "angle" so that whilst we usually regard a polygon as being comprised of **many sides** it is more accurate to describe it as a geometric shape having **many angles.**

The main polygons are described as follows:

NO. of ANGLES and SIDES	NAME OF POLYGON
3	Triangle
4	Quadrilateral or Tetragon
5	Pentagon
6	Hexagon or Sexagon
7	Heptagon or Septagon
8	Octagon
9	Nonagon
10	Decagon
11	Hendecagon or Undecagon
12	Dodecagon
15	Pentadecagon or Quindecagon
20	Icosagon

Fig. 1

Collective numbers

There is a class of numerical term which indicates a collection or a shared characteristic. Included in this category are words such as *both, a pair, a couple, a duplicate, twins, a duet, a brace, triplets, quadruplets, a triad, a dozen, a score, a gross, legion* (from the Roman Army of antiquity) and *myriad* (from the Greek numeral – the GK suffix *-ad* denoting a group).

Brace, meaning "a couple or a pair or two things when taken together", has its root in the IE *braghu* (short) from which we derive words such as *arm* (the upper arm being shorter than the forearm – compare the French *bras*), *bracelet* and *embrace*.

The word *score* comes from the IE *(s)ker*, to scratch or cut, and the Old Norse *skor*, a tally, mark or notch. By extension, *skor* had the meaning of the number 20 by reference to the ancient wooden tally or counting stick on which notches were made to keep a record of the number of livestock or other provisions measured in fives (four vertical notches with a fifth across them) where each stick was used for a maximum of 20 notches. By further extension (but not until the eighteenth century), *score* also came to be used to indicate the tally in many sports and games although in Strutt's *Sports and Pastimes of the People of England* (1834) the author manages to describe the rules of "foot-ball" and the rules of cricket without any use of the word *score*.

Some other collective number words are set out in columns 14 to 18 in Fig. 2 on page 143.

Number systems

Words describing number systems are set out in columns 12 and 13 in Fig. 2, all of which derive from Latin.

The term *undecimal* has the appearance of a negative whereas it is a compound of the Latin *uni-* meaning "one" and *decimal* meaning "ten", literally one more than ten. The word *duodenum* (similar to *duodenary*), being the first part of the small intestine, was so called by reference to the Latin *duodenum digitorum*, meaning a space of 12 fingers which approximates to its length.

Fractional or partitive numbers

Fractional numbers are numbers which describe the result of dividing a whole number and include words such as *half, third, quarter, fifth, two-ninths*.

Half is the subject of Chapter 10½.

1	2	3	4	5	6	7	8	9	10	11
Cardinal numbers		Ordinal numbers			Ranking numbers		Multiplicative and replicative numbers			
No.	word	No.	adj.	adverb	adj.	adverb	adj.	adj.	adj.	adj.
0	zero, nil, nought	0	zeroth						empty	
1	one	1st	first	firstly	primary	once	onefold	simplex	single, solo, singleton, monuple	single
2	two	2nd	second	secondly	secondary	twice	twofold	duplex	couple, double, twin, dual	duplicate
3	three	3rd	third	thirdly	tertiary	thrice	threefold	triplex	triple, triad, treble, trial, trinal, trine	triplicate
4	four	4th	fourth	fourthly	quaternary		fourfold	quadruplex	quadruple, quadral	quadruplicate
5	five	5th	fifth	fifthly	quinary		fivefold	quintuplex	quintuple, pentadruple, pentuple	quintuplicate
6	six	6th	sixth	sixthly			sixfold	sextuplex	sextuple, hexatruple, hextuple	sextuplicate
7	seven	7th	seventh	seventhly			sevenfold	septuplex	septuple, heptuple	
8	eight	8th	eighth	eighthly			eightfold	octuplex	octuple	
9	nine	9th	ninth	ninthly			ninefold	nonuplex	noncuple, nonuple	
10	ten	10th	tenth	tenthly			tenfold	decemplex	decuple	
11	eleven	11th	eleventh	eleventhly			elevenfold		undecuple, hendecuple	
12	twelve	12th	twelfth, dozenth	twelfthly			twelvefold		duodecuple	
13	thirteen	13th	thirteenth	thirteenthly					tredecuple	
14	fourteen	14th	fourteenth	fourteenthly					quattuordecuple	
15	fifteen	15th	fifteenth	fifteenthly					quindecuple	
16	sixteen	16th	sixteenth	sixteenthly					sexdecuple	
17	seventeen	17th	seventeenth	seventeenthly					sedecuple, septendecuple	
18	eighteen	18th	eighteenth	eighteenthly					octodecuple	
19	nineteen	19th	nineteenth	nineteenthly					novemdecuple	
20	twenty	20th	twentieth				twentyfold		vigintuple	
ANSWERS THE QUESTION:										
How many are there?		What position does it hold?			What rank or level of importance does it have?	How many times does it occur?	What is the magnitude of multiplication?	Of how many parts or sections does it consist?	What is the quality of the item in the set?	What is the nature of the item in the set?

12	13	14	15	16	17	18	19	20	21	22
Number systems		Collective numbers					Groups		Fractions	No.
adj.	adj.	noun	noun	noun	noun	noun	noun	noun		
				nihility	void		nothingness			0
unary	unal	unit	solo	unity	singleton	single	oneness	monad	whole	1
binary	binal	doublet, twin	duet	duality, couple, pair, duo	doubleton	twosome	twoness	dyad	half	2
ternary	ternal, tertial, trinal	triplet	trio	trinity, trio	tripleton	threesome	threeness	triad	third	3
quaternary	quaternal, quartal	quadruplet	quartet	quaternity, quadruplicity, quaternion		foursome	fourness	tetrad	quarter	4
quinary	quintal	quintuplet	quintet			fivesome	fiveness	pentad	fifth	5
senary, sexenary	sextal	sextuplet	sextet			sixsome	sixness	hexad	sixth	6
septenary	septimal	septuplet	septet			sevensome	sevenness	heptad	seventh	7
octonary	octal, octimal, octaval	octuplet	octet			eightsome	eightness	octad	eighth	8
nonary, novenary	nonal	nonuplet	nonet			ninesome	nineness	ennead	ninth	9
denary, decenary	decimal	decuplet	dectet			tensome		decad	tenth	10
undenary	undecimal							hendecad	eleventh	11
duodenary	duodecimal						twelveness	duodecad	twelfth	12
							thirteenness		thirteenth	13
							fourteenness		fourteenth	14
							fifteenness		fifteenth	15
						sixteensome			sixteenth	16
	septendecimal								seventeenth	17
									eighteenth	18
									nineteenth	19
vicenary	vigesimal, icosian								twentieth	20

ANSWERS THE QUESTION:

What basis of reckoning is used?	What is the quality of the item in the set?	Of what description is the group of musicians?	Of what quality is the set?	What is the quality of each member of the set?	Of what description is the set?	What property does the group have?	What is the nature of the group?	Of what fraction does the item consist?

Fig. 2

18
NUMBER AND ITS B

The intrusive B

Why, if the word *number* derives from the Latin *numerus,* is it spelt with the interpolation of the letter B? We do not find this in any other words derived from *numerus* such as *numeral, enumerate, numerology* and *numerous.*

It seems likely that the intrusive letter B was inserted in the seventeenth century merely to achieve a smoother pronunciation and conformity with words such as *comb.* Indeed, this process is not uncommon and can be seen in many words such as:

nimble	from the IE root *nem,* quick at seizing
ramble	OE *romen,* to roam
limb	ME *lim*
grumble	IE *ghrem,* to thunder
humble	L *humilis*

N's appearing and disappearing act

The letter N has likewise been introduced into words such as:

messenger	derived from *message*
passenger	derived from *passage*
scavenger	altered form of *scavager*

popinjay	from *popejay*
nickname	derived from *ekename*
nightingale	from *nightegale*

In contrast, by a process referred to as "folk change" or aphaeresis, the letter N has, over time, lost its place at the head of words such as *napron* which became *apron*. It is easy to appreciate why the transposition from *a napron* to *an apron* occurred. Similarly, *a nadder* became *an adder* (*nadr* being Welsh for snake), *ewt* became *newt*, *numpire* became *umpire* and *numbles* became *umbles*, thus bringing us back to *humble*. Similarly, *ice cream* was originally *iced cream* and *mince meat* was originally *minced meat*.

Numb and thumb

There are, of course, two ways of pronouncing the word *number*. When used as a noun we pronounce *number* with the intrusive B whereas when referring to the comparative of *numb* (deprived of feeling) we completely ignore the B.

Although the mathematical *number* and the anatomical *numb* have entirely different meanings they both derive from the same Indo-European root, *nem*, meaning "to apportion, divide, take or allot". *Numb* derives from the sense of being taken, overpowered and ultimately deprived of sensation. Until the 1700s the word *numb* was more usually spelt *num* or *numme*. It appears in the first folio of Shakespeare's *Henry VI* as *numme* – a formulation we preserve in the word *numskull* (a person who is dull-witted).

We see that the long-standing family connection between the two words *number* and *numb* is reawakened by the intrusive B which has managed to infiltrate both words. An intrusive letter of this kind is often described by etymologists as excrescent, meaning "growing out", but which, in its lexicological sense, indicates a sound developed for the sake of euphony and having no etymological significance.

Other examples of excrescence are provided by words such as *bound, hound, round, sound* and *mould*, each of which has an excrescent D; and *amidst, amongst, against* and *whilst* which have an excrescent T. Also, the word *pilchard* has grown a letter D.

Yet another common word which has experienced excrescence is the word *thumb* to which we find the letter B has formed an attachment much in the same way as it has in the word *numb*. *Thumb* is of particular interest to us here because of its relationship with the word *thousand*, the most plausible explanation of which is that it is the result of the union of the IE root *teu/tu* (to swell) and the OE *hund* (a hundred). *Hundred,* itself, is a compound of *hund* and *-red* meaning "a count or reckoning".

Thousand then is "a swollen hundred" or "many hundreds" and is cognate with words such as *tumour, tumulus, tuber, thigh* (a swollen leg) and *thumb* (a swollen finger).

A number of other meanings

Why do we use the word *number* to refer to a song, tune or piece of music, particularly in a recording or performance? The answer may be that in any sequence of items (like the acts set out in a vaudeville theatre programme) it would not be unusual for those items to be numbered and that, indeed, is why individual periodical publications, being one of a series, are often referred to as "numbers".

However, the answer to the question is less prosaic since the word *number* was used from Elizabethan times until the nineteenth century to indicate metrical feet, harmony, verse or poetry in reference to poetical rhythm with its reliance on counting.

Why do we call the fourth book of the Old Testament "Numbers"? It is so called because it contains the details of the census carried out by the Israelites during the Exodus.

The word *number* figures in numerous slang expressions including "I've got your number" indicating that the speaker knows the characteristics of the person he is addressing or, more sinisterly, that he knows where that person lives so making an implicit threat. "Your number is up" indicates either unpleasant consequences or, its opposite, a lottery win. The phrase "to do a number" means to go to jail and to have a "cushy number" is to have an easy job where *number* is used in the sense of a task, a job or a performance.

Our developing number system

The remoulding of numbers cannot occur in the same way as words and language regularly come to be reshaped. Adding digits to the beginning, or to the middle or the end of a string of numbers is hardly likely to maintain the integrity of that string.

There are, nonetheless, many respects in which numbers can be seen as undergoing a form of mutation.

The European number system with its digits 0 to 9 has taken more than four thousand years to evolve into the numerals with which we are now so familiar. However, the development of numerals into a form which we might only faintly recognise did not come into being until about a thousand years ago.

Our numerals originated in India and were embraced by the Arab world which reformulated them and finally exported them to Europe via Spain and North Africa. Throughout this evolutionary period, our numerals took on many different shapes and sizes before settling down to their current form. In their travels through the Arab world, such variation was only to be expected, having regard to the many different kinds of mathematical computation used by merchants and mathematicians. At this time there was nothing to encourage standardisation or consistency in numerals in the same way as, for example, the printing press would eventually come to influence the form of the alphabet and the spelling of the written word.

The story of the development of zero is the most fascinating of these tales for its conception and evolution have revolutionised mathematics as no other number has. Conceived separately by the Mesopotamians and the Mayans, zero had life breathed into it by the Indian world sending it on its way through China and the Arab world so as to reach Western Europe in the twelfth century.

Extraordinarily, the Greeks largely managed without it and the Roman world had no name for it; yet mathematics and science could not manage without it.

Further changes in our numerals of the same degree of importance are most unlikely. However, new technologies and the growing requirement to accommodate the migration of the printed word (and number) from paper to digital format indicate that the evolutionary process is far from complete. Indeed, the rate at which new fonts and typefaces are being created is just one example of why we might expect an accelerated growth in the different ways in which we might come to depict our numerals.

Rounding and truncation

In everyday usage there are changes we regularly make to numbers which are accepted as normal and helpful but which are effected at the cost of precision and certainty. Such changes are made according to the conventions of rounding and truncation which are applied in the process of creating, storing, recording and manipulating numbers either on paper or electronically. These conventions are applied when the accuracy of a particular number is in doubt or when a number is more precise than is required. They are also regularly applied, for example, in journalism and in the media to avoid pedantry and to facilitate a pithy headline. But there are no hard and fast rules.

In mathematics and science, the conventions for rounding and significant figures have to be far more precise than is required in everyday writing and their complex rules are not appropriate for discussion here.

For everyday purposes rounding involves either rounding up or rounding down variously to the nearest unit, ten, hundred, thousand, million or, for example, to the nearest pound, mile, ton or other unit of measurement. Rounding also applies to decimal numbers.

The rounding of whole numbers is used, for example, where the writer is in a position to be able to sacrifice accuracy for catchiness. "Nearly 80,000 spectators attended the opening ceremony of the Rio Olympics" is a far more attractive headline than "78,838 spectators attended..." which has a slightly different emphasis.

The rounding of decimal numbers serves a variety of other purposes including the need to avoid extending the length of a number beyond the required number of digits allotted to it. Rounding will usually be carried out by reference to a chosen number of decimal places so as to provide a shorter replacement number which is close to the original. The rounding of money values is, of course, desirable to avoid referring to, say, £27.34789. Conventionally that figure would be rounded **up** to £27.35. £27.3441 would be rounded **down** to £27.34.

One other convention used in mathematics deserves mentioning here. It is the convention that where, in any number which is to be rounded, the last significant digit is 5, then we round to the nearest **even** digit. Hence, 825 rounded to the nearest ten (that is to two significant figures) would be rounded **down** to 820 while 835 rounded to the nearest ten would be rounded **up** to 840. This convention would ensure, for example, that companies paying dividends would be unlikely to be required to pay an aggregate amount exceeding the aggregate amount of the declared dividend since, in any rounding exercise carried out by a company to determine the amount payable to each of its shareholders, half of those payments would be expected to have been rounded down and half rounded up.

According to most conventions:

22.5	to the nearest whole number would be rounded up to 23 or rounded down to 22 according to "the rules of the house"
22.5	rounded to the nearest ten would become 20
£12.06	rounded down to the nearest pound is £12
£11.85	rounded up to the nearest pound is £12
407.7	rounded to the nearest whole number is 408
0.494	to the nearest whole number is 0
2.9453	rounded to two decimal places is 2.95
9,783	to the nearest thousand equals 10,000
8,438.69	would become 8,000, 8,400, 8,439 or 8,438.7 according to the required degree of rounding

Truncation, which involves a similar exercise, merely operates to delete the digits for which there is insufficient room in the medium being used so that, for example, 27.346448 becomes 27.34 if there is room on the spreadsheet for only four digits and rounding is not required. The excess digits 6448 merely disappear with truncation whereas with rounding the number 27.346448 would have become 27.35.

To ponder...

An ancient tale is told of a father who left all his horses by his Will to his three sons in the following fractions: **A** ½, **B** ⅓ and **C** ⅑. He died leaving 17 horses and a distraught family unable to work out how to give effect to the father's Will. Along came their enlightened lawyer who rounded up the 17 horses in more ways than one. He temporarily loaned the estate an extra horse from his own stable, thus increasing the total number of horses to 18. In consequence, the horses could be distributed as follows:

Son **A** received ½ = 9 horses

Son **B** ⅓ = 6 horses

Son **C** ⅑ = 2 horses

The total number of horses which were thus distributed came to 17 making it possible for the lawyer both to satisfy the sons and to take back the one horse he had lent them. All of which goes to show that either the person who drafted the Will could not add fractions together or that he did not spot the typing error where ⅑ should have read ⅙.

However, without that inspired error, there would have been no means of producing such a satisfying outcome.

19
NUMBER OR WORD?

Correct usage

Nowhere is the connection between numbers and words more intertwined than on those occasions where they can be employed as alternatives in any text where there is a choice between representing a number either as a figure or as a word.

That choice will rarely involve any linguistic or grammatical considerations since whether we choose to write "This is a sentence of 42 words" or "This is a sentence of forty-two words" there would be no compromise of meaning or loss of clarity. Likewise, the choice can hardly be said to depend on any mathematical requirement. The choice will merely depend on style; a concern to which the many published correct usage guides devote much space.

Relegating the question merely to a matter of style does not, however, mean that the choice is made any easier.

Where the correct formulation of any particular sentence depends on consideration of its grammatical structure there is normally a simple choice between what is considered grammatically correct or grammatically incorrect. Likewise, in mathematics, there is usually either a correct answer or a wrong answer.

This is not so in matters of style where the formulation of any rule regarding the writing of text is far more complex. That complexity is only to be expected where such rules will need to take into account:

*   the type of publication in which the text is to appear. Newspaper or journalistic style is different from that applied in fiction, academic journals, mathematical publications, legal texts and children's books;

- the house style of each publisher will be different from the next if only because of their own preferences;
- the differences in style between British and American usage, particularly when it comes to the expression of numbers. For example, the number 123 is usually expressed in British vernacular as "one hundred and twenty-three" but in the US as "one twenty three";
- whether the words occur as reported speech or dialogue;
- the fact that numbers, as they appear in text, are used in many different ways and for many different purposes. They may be used to indicate a precise number or an approximation; they may be used to indicate a small number or a large number; to represent quantity, measurement, order, time or space; as a percentage or as decimals; to indicate an address or telephone number; or in an idiomatic or colloquial sense.

Firm rules are therefore impossible when there are so many circumstances to provide for. Indeed, with some rules of style, the extent of their exceptions serves to suffocate the initial rule to a point where we may question its right to exist.

And yet no publication can expect to maintain standards and consistency without some rules or, at least, a set of "recommendations" for its contributors. One particular publication encourages its contributors to "screw the rules" but such encouragement occurs on page 95 of a publication of 158 pages setting out its preferred usage.

The following set of rules culled from the guides to good English referred to in the Bibliography are intended to answer various common problems of usage including the correctness, in text, of using the number or the word and the handling of numbers. They are merely a guide and are not prescriptive:

Rule 1
Avoid blind adherence to **any** rule (except this one). The need to apply common sense to any particular choice should always be in mind as should the need for clarity and the need to avoid ambiguity and awkwardness.

Rule 2
Seek to achieve consistency but without being a slave to it.

Rule 3
Write *one* to *ten* as words rather than numbers except:

- where the numbers occur in clusters as in: "the ages of the participants were 9, 12, 14 and 15";
- where there would be a loss of consistency as in: "The allocation was increased from 7 to 17". Alternatively, we can write "from seven to seventeen";
- where the figure itself is the subject matter as in "the number 7 is sometimes written as 7 with a dash through it to distinguish it from 1";
- when combining digits and words with a hyphen in certain set phrases such as "4-wheel drive";
- in sums of money, which are expressed in figures such as £7;
- when referring to decimal figures, so 8.25;
- with fractions used in combination with whole numbers as in 8½ but one-quarter and two-thirds;
- in legal documents, both words and numerals are sometimes used together so as to reduce the possibility of error, hence "£5,000 (five thousand pounds)".

The threshold of ten is often increased for the purpose of this rule to 100.

Rule 4
When using the ordinals first to tenth, write them out as words except where they occur as dates so 16th July 1975.

Rule 5
Express the cardinal numbers from 11 onwards as numerals rather than as words ("I have read 154 pages") except:

- where consistency would be sacrificed (see rule 3);
- where the number occurs at the beginning of the sentence so: "Thirty students were awarded prizes". As an alternative, we can rephrase to say: "Prizes were awarded to 30 students";
- where there is imprecision as in: "I've told you a thousand times";
- where it helps to avoid confusion as in: "twelve 3-room apartments";
- in colloquial phrases such as "they were a million miles apart";
- where the subject of the text is the number itself as in: "The American billion consists of 1 followed by nine zeros";
- where any large number is expressed in two or more words as in: "The forest contains three million trees";
- where quantities are being used, for example in a recipe;
- in expressing the time as in "twenty past nine".

Rule 6

Reverse the application of rules 3 and 5 when dealing with ages so: "a boy of 7" and "a woman in her thirties".

Rule 7

Refer to midnight as 12 a.m. or 24.00 or 12 midnight. Midday should be expressed as 12 p.m., 12.00 or 12 noon.

Rule 8

Abbreviate million etc. to *m* only in headlines.

Rule 9

Unless more precision is required, round numbers up or down to two decimal places (see page 149) or to the nearest hundred, thousand or million etc.

Rule 10

When writing numbers of more than four digits in non-technical matter it is usually best in separating the thousands to use commas (e.g. 204,010) although in many countries a comma is used to indicate a decimal point so that inserting a thin space may be preferable (as in, 204|010 thus 204 010) in some cases. A comma can also help clarification in four-digit numbers other than dates.

Rule 11

Compound numbers, whether cardinal or ordinal, from twenty-one onwards, usually carry a hyphen whether or not used as part of a larger number so: sixty-seven, seventy-sixth and one hundred and ninety-nine.

Some other conventions regarding numbers

Firstly, when we use the expression "number of" should it be followed by a singular or plural noun?

The answer depends on whether the phrase is either "**A** number of" or "**The** number of".

"A number of…" takes the plural as in: "A number of demonstrators are carrying placards" and "There is a small number of demonstrators carrying placards".

However, "**The** number of..." anticipates the singular as in: "The number of demonstrators is small" and "The number of demonstrators who are holding placards is small".

Secondly, Fowler tells us that in enumerating sequences it is just as acceptable to use **firstly**, *secondly* and *thirdly* as it is to use **first**, *secondly* and *thirdly* where possibly the initial opposition to using *firstly* originated from the fact that Samuel Johnson did not include the word in his *Dictionary of the English Language*, first published in 1755.

Finally, how should we use *No.* – an abbreviation of the word *number*? Judging by the fact that the term is not mentioned until the last of the 1,638 pages of Longman's massive *A Comprehensive Grammar of the English Language*, it appears that there are no firm rules. *No.* is a contraction of the L *numero* and takes many forms including *Nº*, *Nº*, *No* and *no.* (as does its plural *Nos.*) and in each case is pronounced in its long form. It should not be used if it might be confused with "no", (the negative), the element Nobelium or expressions such as navigation officer, the natural order or New Orleans and certainly not in phrases such as "No one is the winner" if what you really mean is "No.1 is the winner". *No.* is best used in informal language with cardinal numbers to indicate addresses, telephone numbers, bus routes, symphonies and the like where an identification of some kind is being made rather than a reference to a quantity or to a calculation. In the U.S. the hash (#), or so-called *octothorpe*, is more commonly used to identify numbers.

20
PYRAMID PUZZLES

The pyramid puzzle

A once regular feature in *The Times* was a puzzle requiring the application of some straightforward logic. The puzzle involves a triangular pattern in the form of a pyramid of 15 shaded cells as in Fig. 1 below with numbers set out in some of those cells.

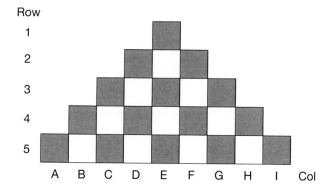

Fig. 1

The task is to work out the value of the top cell in row 1 where the value in any of the ten shaded cells in rows 1 to 4 is equal to the addition of the two cells immediately below it. Hence, if we know the value of all the cells in row 5 the process of finding the value of the top cell will purely be a mechanical one.

If, for example, the values of the five cells in row 5 were respectively 4, 2, 8, 12 and 1, the value of the top cell would be 109 as follows in Fig. 2 arrived at by the simple exercise of carrying out successive additions – the value of the first cell in row 4 is 6 being the addition of the 4 and the 2 supporting it, and so on.

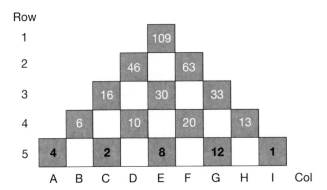

Fig. 2

The task becomes more interesting when the value of some of the cells in row 5 is omitted and, instead, values are given for cells in a row higher up in the pyramid as, for example, in Figs. 3 and 4:

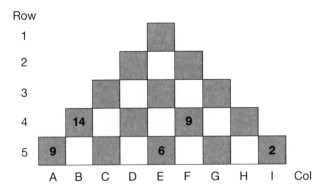

Fig. 3

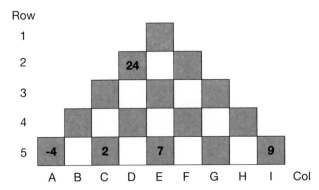

Fig. 4 (Note that cell A5 is a negative)

These two pyramids with their remaining values completed are set out on pages 214 and 215. **Question T**.

By including minus numbers in row 5 we add another level of interest; and so could we if the task set is to insert such numbers in row 5 as will produce a given number in row 1; or to produce an Excel spreadsheet which automatically fills in the requisite numbers in a similar way to that referred to on page 72.

What is the **minimum** amount of information we need to calculate the top cell? Each of the two examples in Fig. 3 and Fig. 4 contains values for five cells. Can the task be accomplished with less than five known values? If we assume that no one value in row 5 is repeated, we can make do with only three values. You may wish to try this with the following pyramid, the full set of values for which is set out on pages 215 and 216 (**Question U**) together with a method for working it out:

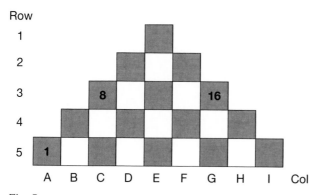

Fig. 5

Without wishing to spoil the fun, there is a simple formula to enable us to calculate the value of the top cell if all of the cells in row 5 are known (and even if some or all of them are minus numbers). The value of the top cell will be equal to:

(Cell 5A x 1) + (Cell 5C x 4) + (Cell 5E x 6) + (Cell 5G x 4) + (Cell 5I x 1)

The multiples for these five cells are thus: **1   4   6   4   1**

The multiples for similar pyramids vary according to the number of cells as follows:

Number of cells in the bottom row	Total number of cells	Required multiples for each cell in the bottom row						
1	1				1			
2	3			1		1		
3	6			1	2	1		
4	10		1	3	3	1		
5	15		1	4	6	4	1	
6	21	1	5	10	10	5	1	
7	28	1	6	15	20	15	6	1

Fig. 6

The pattern of the multiples (or, more properly, multiplicands) in each row in Fig. 6 is fascinating because it can be generated by taking 11 to successive powers so that $11^0 = 1$, $11^1 = 11$, $11^2 = 121$, $11^3 = 1{,}331$ and $11^4 = 14{,}641$. The number 11 raised to further successive powers also generates a recognisable pattern.

Pascal

Even more importantly, the pattern is recognisable as the famous Pascal's triangle, created by Blaise Pascal and published posthumously in 1664 – although its origins are thought to be much older.

Pascal's triangle starts at the top with a 1. Each successive row below it has one additional number so that the row below the first has two numbers, the next three and so on. Each row begins and ends with 1. The numbers encompassed within each pair of 1s is arrived at by adding together the two supported numbers to its left and right in the row immediately above so as to form a symmetrical pattern as in Fig. 7 below.

Shallow diagonals add up to:	PASCAL'S TRIANGLE	Rows add up to:
1	1	1
	1 1	2
2	1 2 1	4
	1 3 3 1	8
5	1 4 6 4 1	16
	1 5 10 10 5 1	32
13	1 6 15 20 15 6 1	64
	1 7 21 35 35 21 7 1	128
34	1 8 28 56 70 56 28 8 1	256

Fig. 7

Pascal's triangle has relevance and application in many fields of mathematics. However, it is also notable how often Pascal's triangle and its various properties occur in recreational maths as can be seen, for example, in this chapter and in Chapter 8 where Pascal provides a solution to the question as to how many different routes may be taken on a grid on moving from one point to another.

There is also a resonance with the Fibonacci sequence (see Chapter 26) in that the shallow diagonals of Pascal's triangle (see Fig. 7) add up to Fibonacci numbers. Also, the addition of the numbers in each row (see the last column in Fig. 7 above) is twice the total of the previous row. More surprisingly the aggregate of the numbers in each row can be expressed successively as 2^0, 2^1, 2^2, 2^3, 2^4, 2^5, 2^6, 2^7 and 2^8 where the relevant power is located in each case in the penultimate number in the row. Hence, the aggregate of the numbers in the last line can be found by calculating 2 to the power 8.

To ponder...

Another triangle which appears, at first sight, to be related to Pascal's triangle is the following:

ROW	SEQUENCE
1	1
2	11
3	21
4	1211
5	111221
6	312211
7	13112221
8	?

Fig. 8

However, Fig. 8 has nothing to do with Pascal. It is a fascinating puzzle which requires row 8 of the pyramid to be completed by reference to some logical process. Some find the puzzle difficult to solve so here are three clues.

Clue 1: Turn off any facility for converting text to speech.

Clue 2: Row 1 is the only true number.

Clue 3: Although the puzzle is not strictly a sequence, each row has a special relationship with the previous one.

The answer is on page 216. **Question V**.

Word pyramids

Pyramids also feature in many word games such as the following.

The task, starting at the top of the pyramid with any letter of the alphabet, is, progressively, to add one further letter to the transposed letters of the previous level so as to form a new word.

Hence:

```
                        A
                    A       T
                T       A       G
            G       A       T       E
        A       G       E       N       T
    N       E       G       A       T       E
T       E       E       N       A       G       E
G       E       N       E       R       A       T       E
A       G       R       E       E       M       E       N       T
R       E       G       A       L       E       M       E       N       T
E   N       L       A       R       G       E       M       E       N       T
E   N   L       A       R       G       E       M       E       N       T       S
```

Fig. 9

To make the task more difficult, the requirement may be to ensure that every word **ends** with the same letter as in the following example:

```
                        T
                    E       T
                N       E       T
            R       E       N       T
        I       N       E       R       T
    I       N       S       E       R       T
R       E       S       I       A       N       T
A       N       G       R       I       E       S       T
G       R       A       I       N       I       E       S       T
```

Fig. 10

... or **begins** with the same letter as in:

```
                        R
                    R       E
                R       E       T
            R       E       S       T
        R       E       S       E       T
    R       E       S       T       E       D
R       E       S       I       T       E       D
R       E       S       I       S       T       E       D
R       E       S       I       D       E       N       T       S
```

Fig. 11

Another variation is to devise a pyramid where both the letters across and the letters down spell words, as in the following pyramids where two extra letters are added at each level (all words used being allowed in Scrabble®):

```
              L
           C  U  D
        M  O  R  O  N
        M  O  N  I  T  O  R
     F  O  U  N  D  E  R  E  D
```

Fig. 12

```
              F
           D  A  B
        C  O  R  E  R
        H  O  V  E  R  E  D
     D  A  R  E  D  E  V  I  L
```

Fig. 13

21
MAGIC SQUARES

Puzzle squares

Magic squares come in one shape but in many sizes.

One simple kind of magic square became popular in the puzzle pages of the *London Evening Standard* some years ago. The puzzle involved a grid of 3 x 3 with just one of the nine cells completed and required the reader to fill in the other eight cells with a set of consecutive numbers so that each row, column and diagonal would add up to the same number – that particular quality constituting the "magical" quality of the square.

A typical example of this puzzle might involve a grid with only one given cell completed (say, the digit 28, as in Fig. 1) and with the task to place all the consecutive numbers from 22 to 30 so as to ensure that each line of three squares (whether across, down or diagonal) will add up to 78.

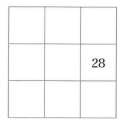

Fig. 1

Those who enjoy the task of finding a solution by trial and error can check their answer over the page. Those who begrudge the time but cannot resist having a go at solving newspaper puzzles may wish to know that there is a method which produces an answer within seconds.

Any magic square with an uneven number of cells, whether 3 x 3 or 103 x 103, can be completed using the following technique. Let us take the grid in Fig. 2 with the numbers 1 to 9 to illustrate the method where each line adds up to 15:

8	1	6
3	5	7
4	9	2

Fig. 2

The technique for completing such a grid involves the following procedure:

Rule A
We start by inserting the first number of the sequence (here number 1) in the middle cell of the top row. (Rotating the grid, of course, means we can, in fact, start from any middle cell on the edge of any cell).

Rule B
Rule B is the basic rule. It requires that we insert the next consecutive number by going to the cell or point immediately northeast of where we have placed the first number. The rest of the rules are merely exceptions to this basic rule. Rule B must be addressed each time.

Rule C
If the consequence of following rule B would take you to a point outside of the grid then, instead, we drop down from that point to the bottom of the column in which that point occurs.

Rule D
If following the procedures in rules B and C, we still find ourselves at a point outside the grid, then we move across to the first cell in the row which rule B brings us.

Rule E
If the procedure in B cannot be adopted because the cell immediately northeast of it has already been taken by a previous number, then we drop down to the cell immediately below that previous number.

Rule F

If the result of following rules B, C and D would still leave us at a point outside the grid, then we drop down to the cell immediately below the previous number.

The procedure may, at first blush, seem complicated but a few minutes' practice will illustrate how simple it is. Let us apply the above rules to show, for example, how Fig. 2 was completed:

No. 1   Insert the first number, 1, in the top middle cell. Rule A.

No. 2   Applying rule B to insert number 2 (by going to the point which is northeast of 1) would bring us to a point outside the grid so we have to slide down to the bottom of the row where 2 would otherwise have been placed. Rule C.

No. 3   When we try to follow rule B in inserting 3 we again end up outside of the grid at a point which is not within a column. So, we slide along to the end of the column in which 3 would otherwise have gone. Rule D.

No. 4   Going northeast of 3 in accordance with rule B is not possible because that cell is occupied by number 1. So we simply drop down to the cell immediately below 3. Rule E.

No. 5   In inserting number 5, we apply rule B and go northeast. Rule B.

No. 6   In inserting the next consecutive number, 6, we again apply rule B and continue to go northeast. Rule B.

No. 7   In the effort to follow rule B when inserting number 7, we are not helped by rules C or D and so we apply rule F and drop down to the cell immediately below 6.

No. 8   We cannot apply rule B in inserting 8 but we can follow rule C.

No. 9   Only one cell is left so this must be the home for number 9 so we place it there in compliance with rule C.

Having practised on Fig. 2 let us return to Fig. 1 and, following the same procedure, place the first of the nine consecutive numbers in the middle cell of the top row and follow the above procedure. If this does not allow for the given number to appear where it is placed, then the grid can be rotated so that it can fit in.

With just a little practice it becomes easier to place each consecutive number to the point where you will be trying larger grids. However, this particular method applies only to square grids with an **odd** number of cells.

The answer is:

29	22	27
24	26	28
25	30	23

Fig. 3

A short cut

Is there any simple method to work out the sum arrived at by adding together the numbers in each row, column and diagonal of such a magic square? There is. If you take any such magic square with an odd number of cells and starting with the value 1, the sum of the digits in each completed line will always be equal to the result of multiplying the value in the middle square (in Fig. 2 this is 5) by the value in the cell immediately southwest of the cell in which 1 occurs (in Fig. 2 this is 3).

Hence, in a 3 x 3 matrix starting with number 1 as in Fig. 2, all rows, columns and diagonals will add up to 5 x 3 = 15.

With a magic square with consecutive numbers not starting with 1, the sum will be equal to:

x + (*n* (*f* - 1))

Where:

x = the sum which would apply if the set of numbers begins with 1 (that is, 15 in a 3 x 3 matrix)

n = the number of cells in any row

f = the first number in the set

Hence, in Fig. 3 the magic number is: 15 + (3(22-1)) = **78** which, indeed, is the number arrived at by adding the three numbers in any of the rows (including the two diagonals).

... And another word game

A 5 x 5 grid is the starting point for one of the best word games for two players (although it can also be played by three) requiring no more than pencils and paper.

The players each prepare their own 5 x 5 grid.

Player 1 (let us assume there are only two players) chooses any letter of the alphabet and calls it out to the other player. Each player inserts that letter anywhere on his or her own grid, which is not shown to the other until the end of the game.

Player 2 then chooses the next letter and each of them likewise inserts that second letter onto his grid. This goes on until 24 of the 25 squares have been completed. After 24 letters have been inserted in this way, each player can choose his own letter to put into the grid as the twenty-fifth and last entry.

The object is to create as many five-, four- or three-letter words as possible reading across or down. A five-letter word scores 5 points, a four-letter word scores 4 and a three-letter word scores 3. One- and two- letter words do not score. Only one score is allowed per line so that PLANE scores 5 with nothing being added for PLAN or LANE. The player with the higher score is the winner.

Once a letter is placed onto the grid it cannot be removed or altered. Once a letter is chosen by a player it must immediately be inserted onto the grid. "Stockpiling" is strictly forbidden. You can choose whatever rules you like regarding allowable words. Words allowed in Scrabble® would be a good place to start so that proper names and foreign words would be excluded.

Here is an example of a completed game showing the grid of one of the players so as to explain the scoring:

Points:						
5	C	A	T	E	R	
5	A	R	O	S	E	
4	M	E	A	N	A	
5	E	A	S	E	L	
0	L	W	T	T	O	
19acr+21dwn	5	4	5	3	4	**40**

Fig. 4

Anything over 35 is a good score.

There are many different strategies. Whichever you select you must try to maintain as much flexibility as possible so as to cater as best you can for the possibility that your opponent will call out awkward letters.

If **you** were to select Js, Xs or Zs this might be awkward for your opponent, but could cause problems as you, too, would have to accommodate the same letters in your grid.

22

SOME TRIVIAL CONNECTIONS

Trivial – the word

This chapter contains some trivial, but nonetheless engaging connections between numbers and words.

The word *trivial* itself constitutes just one of these. *Trivial*, meaning "of little importance", comes from the L *trivium* (*tri-*, three and *via*, ways) being the place where three roads and its travellers might happen to meet and gossip, suggesting things which are inconsequential, commonplace or vulgar. *Trivial* is often used as a synonym for *trifling* but the two words have no etymological connection since *trifling* comes from the OE *tryfle* meaning "a jest or gibe".

Straight lines

In a number of typefaces, there are a few numbers which, when printed as a word in capital letters, are comprised exclusively of letters formed by straight lines.

TEN, for example, uses nine straight lines and ELEVEN employs 19. No number higher than NINETY-NINE can be spelt without using at least one curved letter. TWENTY-NINE is the most interesting straight-line number since it is the only one which (ignoring the hyphen) uses the same number of straight lines as the number itself.

ONE is the only number which accurately describes the number of curved letters in its name.

Several numbers consisting only of straight lines can be added together to generate the same effect so that, for example:

NO.	THE NUMBER AS A WORD	STRAIGHT LINES USED
20	TWENTY	18
19	NINETEEN	24
10	TEN	9
10	TEN	9
10 +	TEN	9 +
69	SIXTY-NINE	69

– where the aggregate of the above five numbers (69) is equal to the aggregate number of straight lines required to form them.

Number of letters

In the same vein, the number *four* is special because it is the only number which describes its own length, that is, four letters. Whilst there are no other discrete numbers having this particular quality, one can construct many number phrases which do. Looking for self-descriptive phrases of this kind can be fun. Here are some examples:

FIVE PLUS EIGHT	(13 letters)
FOUR AND EIGHT	(12 letters)
FOUR AND SIX	(10 letters)
SIXTEEN MINUS ONE	(15 letters)
SEVENTEEN LESS ONE	(16 letters)
ONE HALF OF THIRTY	(15 letters)
ONE TIMES FIFTEEN	(15 letters)
SEVENTEEN TIMES ONE	(17 letters)
HUNDRED DIVIDED BY FIVE	(20 letters)
TEN LETTERS	(10 letters)
TWO CUBED	(8 letters)

– and a self-referential statement such as: "This sentence has thirty-one letters."

Victor Borge

There are many ways in which letters and numbers can be intermingled or manipulated in wordplay or for comic or humorous effect. Victor Borge (1909-2000), the humorist and musician, introduced a routine he called "Inflationary Language" in which any number (or any word sounding like a number), whether a separate word or embedded in another word, would be increased by one to comic effect. Hence "wonderful" became "twoderful" and "create" became "crenine". "Half-sister" became "one and a half-sister" and "tulips" became "threelips". One of his most well-known performances ends: "Get out of here you three-faced triple crosser."

Doublets

One of the best-known diversions invented by Lewis Carroll (1832-1898) – the author of *Alice's Adventures in Wonderland* and *Through The Looking Glass* – is the word game he called Doublets in which a given word is changed one letter at a time to generate a new word of the same length which has some resonance with the original word. Each letter change in the chain must result in an English word. Here is one of Carroll's Doublets changing FOUR into FIVE by way of example:

FOUR	swap R for L
FOUL	swap U for O
FOOL	swap L for T
FOOT	swap O for R
FORT	swap T for E
FORE	swap O for I
FIRE	swap R for V
FIVE	

Here are three others:

ONE	**FOUR**	**BOOM**
ORE	TOUR	BOOT
ORA	TOUT	MOOT
BRA	TORT	MOST
BAA	TORE	MUST
BAN	TONE	**BUST**
BEN	NONE	
TEN	**NINE**	

Rebuses and Dingbats®

Another form of wordplay favoured by Lewis Carroll was the rebus (from the L plural for "things"). This is a word puzzle popular in the eighteenth and nineteenth centuries in which words are represented by a combination of pictures, numbers and symbols requiring the participant, in effect, to decode a message, sentence or idiomatic phrase. Here are some examples (with answers on page 217) of a related species of puzzle called Dingbats®:

LYME NEWCASTLE	1,7,3,9,5 WHELMING
JUSTA144ICE	HIJKLMNO
POToooooooo	MORPHATE
GEGS	CHIMADENA
ONESROH	YOURMOTHERYOUTAKE

Rebuses and Dingbats® often employ numbers in conjunction with letters as, for example, **4T** (forty), **AT 10 U8** (attenuate) and **LMN8** (eliminate). The best puzzles are those that follow closely the rigours of cryptic crosswords with every constituent part being relevant and in a manner which is grammatical and logical.

A well-known rebus reads as follows:

YY UR,	(Too wise you are,
YY UB;	too wise you be;
IC UR YY4ME.	I see you are too wise for me.)

In a similar vein is:

FUNEM?	(Have you any ham?
SVFM.	Yes, we have ham.
FUNEX?	Have you any eggs?
SVFX.	Yes, we have eggs.
OKNVFMNX.	OK then we'll have ham and eggs.)

– and:

Captain BBBB	(Captain Forbes
Sent his CCCC	Sent his forces
To the DD WEST DD.	To the West Indies.)

Interest in rebuses was reinvigorated by the British television programme *Catchphrase*, which ran on ITV between 1986 and 2001, and by a board game called Dingbats®.

Heraldry also uses rebuses, often in the form of a pun. Hence, the Shelley family coat of arms consists of shells; Wellwood, an oak tree growing out of a well; and Fordyce, the depiction of four dice.

Some doggerel

The intermingling of words and numbers which are homophones works to amusing effect in the two following sets of doggerel much loved by children:

1 1 was a racehorse,

2 2 was 1 2.

1 1 1 a race and

2 2 1 1 2.   [Thanks to Pauline Trotter]

– and

1, 2, 3, 4, 5, 6, 7, 8, 10

What about 9?

7 8 9.   [Thanks to Barenaked Ladies, Desperation Records, 2008]

Numbers and initials

Another popular word puzzle, frequently figuring in quizzes, consists of a list of clues composed of a number accompanied by the initials of several words (such as 365 D in a Y) which requires a solution (365 days in a year).

Here are some tougher ones:

88 K on a P   (88 keys on a piano)

6 D of S   (6 degrees of separation)

52 CIAD   (52 cards in a deck)

64 SOACB   (64 squares on a chess board)

Car numbers

When it comes to vehicle numbers, many ingenious devices have been employed to take advantage of the ambiguities mentioned in Chapter 10. Because of the similarity between 5 and S, 1 and I, 3 and E, 8 and B and so on, credible words can be created out of an imaginative combination of the numbers and letters constituting vehicle numbers. So that:

P15 HER   becomes PISHER

APO 110   becomes APOLLO and   [Thanks to Bill Pollock]

M3 YER   becomes MEYER   [Thanks to Meyer Simmonds]

Mondegreens

In a one-innings cricket match between Losely and Winthrop, Losely scored 299 runs. But Winthrop scored 300 and won. How many runs were scored in aggregate?

Every reader will find it easy to come up with the correct answer of 599. However, if you were merely listening to someone reading this question (rather than reading it to yourself) the answer you are likely to come up with would be 600.

Any text which is capable of being misunderstood or misread in this way because of some homonymic confusion is called a mondegreen, a term coined by Sylvia Wright in *Harper's Magazine* in 1954 in reference to a Scottish ballad containing the line "They hae slain the Earl of Murray And Lady Mondegreen", the last three words of which she had understood to be "… and laid him on the green".

A favourite mondegreen is:

She was a tanker
The Countess of Ayr

– which when read aloud is easily misunderstood as:

She was at anchor
The County Surveyor

The popular song "Mairzy Doats", composed in 1943, appears to be a nonsense rhyme:

Mairzy doats and dozy doats
And liddle lamzy divey
A kiddley divey too, wooden you?

However, on closer inspection the rhyme is another example of a mondegreen where the actual words are:

Mares eat oats and does eat oats
And little lambs eat ivy
A kid will eat ivy too, wouldn't you?

However, these all pale into insignificance in the light of the spoof French poems of Van Rooten in his *Mots D'Heures: Gousses, Rames* (Angus and Robertson, 1967). Here, for your slow measured reading (whether or not you speak French), is the first entry in this amazing book:

Un petit d'un petit
S'étonne aux Halles
Un petit d'un petit
Ah! Degrés te fallent
Indolent qui ne sort cesse
Indolent qui ne se mène
Qu'importe un petit d'un petit
Tout Gai de Reguennes.

What does this mean?

Don't give up yet. You will kick yourself! If you need to, turn to page 217 for an explanation: **Question W**.

23
NUMBERS WITHIN NUMBERS, WORDS WITHIN WORDS

A hidden characteristic

Many numbers hide within them a particular characteristic of interest to those who enjoy "messing about" with numbers.

There are numbers (Harshad numbers), the sum of whose individual digits divides exactly into the number itself so that, for example, the sum of the digits of the number 12 equals 3 which divides into 12 without remainder; that is, it is a factor of 12. Another is 126 whose digits add up to 9 which divides exactly into 126.

- There are several instances where consecutive numbers fall into this category so that for example:

  110 is exactly divisible by 2, the sum of its digits
  111 is exactly divisible by 3, the sum of its digits
  112 is exactly divisible by 4, the sum of its digits
  510 is exactly divisible by 6, the sum of its digits
  511 is exactly divisible by 7, the sum of its digits
  512 is exactly divisible by 8, the sum of its digits

- 114 and the next nine numbers which are formed by successively adding 19 will each, when divided by the sum of their digits, produce the same result, namely, 19:

  114 divided by the sum of its digits, 6, equals 19

133 divided by the sum of its digits, 7, equals 19
152 divided by the sum of its digits, 8, equals 19
171 divided by the sum of its digits, 9, equals 19
190 divided by the sum of its digits, 10, equals 19
209 divided by the sum of its digits, 11, equals 19
228 divided by the sum of its digits, 12, equals 19
247 divided by the sum of its digits, 13, equals 19
266 divided by the sum of its digits, 14, equals 19
285 divided by the sum of its digits, 15, equals 19

This arises as a result of two attributes. Firstly, when 114 is divided by 6, the result happens to equal 19. Secondly, when 19 is added to any of the above numbers (114, 133, 152 etc.) the sum of its digits in each case is increased by 1 because the 10s increase by 2 while the units reduce by 1. The **sum** of the digits of each of the numbers in the above series increases by 1 while the numbers themselves increase by 19 and thus continue to be divisible by 19.

- We get a similar result when we add any of 28, 37, 46, 55, 64, 73, 82 and 91 to any number although this appears most vividly with 37 as follows:

333 divided by the sum of its digits, 9, equals 37
370 divided by the sum of its digits, 10, equals 37
407 divided by the sum of its digits, 11, equals 37
444 divided by the sum of its digits, 12, equals 37
481 divided by the sum of its digits, 13, equals 37

In each case, the process involves taking a number and extracting from it another number particular to it (here the sum of its digits) to find out that that sum is a factor of the original number.

Another hidden characteristic

There is a category of numbers which enjoys the satisfying attribute that when each of them is divided, in turn, by each of the numbers 1 to 12 (the "divisor") the result will give a remainder which in each case is equal to one less than that divisor.

How do we find the lowest number which has this characteristic?

We can start by finding a number which will be **exactly** divisible by each of the numbers 1 to 12, that is, without leaving a remainder. A number which would clearly fulfil that requirement is the number which results from multiplying together each of the 12 numbers from 1 to 12. This gives us the gargantuan 479,001,600 (12 factorial or 12!) which must, by definition, be divisible by each of 1, 2, 3, 4, 5, 6, 7, 8, 9, 10, 11 and 12.

However, in order to find a number which is divisible exactly by each of 1 to 12 we do not need such a large number. In the first place, if the number is exactly divisible by 3 and 4 it must also be divisible by 12. So we can dispense with 12 from the list of factors. Nor do we need the 6 since 2 x 3 = 6. Nor do we need 8 since 2 x 4 = 8. Nor 10. Furthermore, we can replace 9 by another 3 since divisibility by 9 will then be met by multiplying the two 3s. We can also replace 4 by two 2s. Finally, the 1 is redundant.

The result of that culling means that we are left with only the following eight factors:

2, 2, 2, 3, 3, 5, 7 and 11.

This collection of prime numbers is such as to ensure that when multiplied together the result will be divisible by all the numbers from 1 to 12. Multiplying these eight numbers together generates the result 27,720 which does, indeed, divide by each of 1 to 12 without leaving any remainder.

However, the task is to find the **lowest** number which leaves a remainder of **one less** than the divisors 1 to 12. To achieve this, we simply deduct 1 from 27,720 to give us 27,719 since, if 27,720 leaves no remainder when divided by any particular divisor, it will leave one less than that divisor if we reduce the number by 1.

If we divide 27,719 by each of 1 to 12 we get the following remainders:

27,719	
when divided by:	leaves a remainder of:
1	0
2	1
3	2
4	3
5	4
6	5
7	6
8	7
9	8
10	9
11	10
12	11

Fig. 1

Even more satisfying is the fact that, if we divide 27,719 by any combination of the 12 factors in Fig. 1, the remainder will always be one less than the product of those factors so that, for example, 27,719 divided by **77** (7 x 11) gives us remainder **76** and 27,719 divided by **462** (2 x 3 x 7 x 11) yields a remainder of **461**.

The process of arriving at 27,719 in this way is most edifying because not only does it show us that the apparently extraordinary characteristic is, after all, not at all unusual, but it also gives us the means to explore and to set ourselves further tasks.

What does it take, for example, to find the lowest number which works in the same way but includes divisors 13, 14, 15 and 16, so that when it is divided by each of 1 to 16 its remainder will again be one less than the divisor?

We know that 27,720 is effective for the numbers up to 12 so that to extend the process to include 13 we need to add that factor to the list. 14 is already met by one of the 2s and the 7, 15 is met by one of the 3s and the 5, but for 16 we need four 2s so we merely add one more. Hence, we have a number which has the following factors: **2**, **2**, **2**, **2**, **3**, **3**, **5**, **7**, **11**, **13**. When multiplied together these produce 720,720.

We need to reduce that number by 1 in order to generate the answer, namely, 720,719. We can test this to see whether it gives the correct results as follows:

720,719	
when divided by:	leaves a remainder of:
1	0
2	1
3	2
4	3
5	4
6	5
7	6
8	7
9	8
10	9
11	10
12	11
13	12
14	13
15	14
16	15

Fig. 2

Hidden words

We can play with words in similar fashion. The following wordplay involves an allied concept whereby we choose a particular word and extract from within it a letter string which itself constitutes a separate word resonating with the chosen word in some way or another. As an example, if we take the word REVENGE, we see that within that word there occurs another word, EVEN, which resonates because of the phrase "to get even with someone". The only other rule in this wordplay is that the shorter word must not occur at the beginning or the end of the chosen word.

Here are some examples:

ache	in	tracheostomy	one	in	abandoned
arc	in	searchlight	Oslo	in	Czechoslovakia
cut	in	charcuterie	other	in	psychotherapy
end	in	appendix	over	in	hovering
emit	in	semitone	pie	in	mouthpiece
error	in	terrorism	rain	in	drainpipe
even	in	seventy-six	red	in	credit
free	in	anti-freeze	rid	in	abridge
hit	in	Whitehall farce	Rome	in	promenade
ill	in	bacillus	tea	in	gateau
itch	in	witch hazel	under	in	foundering
neat	in	delineation	verse	in	oversentimental

We can extend the realms of this wordplay by seeking internal words which exist **in reverse** and which, if possible, resonate in some way with the longer word or phrase within which they are contained.

For example:

arty	in	personality trait	rash	in	Noah's ark
ban	in	enable	renege	in	regenerate
email	in	parliament	son	in	paternoster
ill	in	ebullient	tale	in	revelation
lucid	in	ridiculous	loser	in	unresolved

Beheaded words

Another form of wordplay involves identifying a particular word which when denied its first letter nonetheless continues to have meaning as a discrete word. You can set yourself whatever rules you like. Here is the result of locating 26 words, each beginning with a different letter of the alphabet which, once removed, produces a new word with an entirely different meaning from the original and (in almost all cases) does not rhyme with it:

A	atrophy		N	nascent
B	broadside		O	orange
C	chandler		P	phoney
D	dragged		Qu	quart
E	eastern		R	routing
F	flowering		S	slaughter
G	grant		T	tone
H	herring		U	usage
I	islander		V	vaunt
J	jaunt		W	wrath
K	know		X	xerotic
L	learned		Y	yearly
M	mallow		Z	zeros

"Befooted" words

A similar diversion involves locating a word which, when the **last** of its letters is removed, will nonetheless form a new word with a different meaning. The following list involves removing from the end of the word each of the letters A to Z:

A	drama	**N**	postern
B	proverb	**O**	beano
C	magic	**P**	chump
D	amend	**Q**	talaq
E	diverse	**R**	latter
F	belief	**S**	needless
G	raising	**T**	minutest
H	hearth	**U**	menu
I	lassi	**V**	rev
J	haj	**W**	sinew
K	squawk	**X**	codex
L	carousel	**Y**	blowsy
M	maxim	**Z**	quartz

From beginning to end

One extension of these pursuits involves the task of identifying words of more than four letters which have the quality that, when the first letter is transposed to the end of the word, a new word is created. Hence:

dangle	>>	angled		shopper	>>	hoppers
emanate	>>	manatee		swordplay	>>	wordplays
gratin	>>	rating		stable	>>	tables
heart	>>	earth		stripe	>>	tripes
overs	>>	verso				

The last two examples in the second column above are particularly interesting because they each allow for **two** successive transposals. Starting with STABLE we reach TABLES on the first transposal and ABLEST on the second.

Starting with STRIPE we generate TRIPES on the first transposal and then RIPEST on the next.

This process has a close resonance with the mathematical diversion on page 55 called alphametics. This is best demonstrated by allocating values to each of the six letters in STABLE so that:

S = 1   T = 4   A = 2   B = 8   L = 5   and   E = 7

– thus generating the six-digit cyclic number 142,857 standing for STABLE.

If we now multiply 142,857 by 3 we get 428,571 and then by 2 we get 285,714, which numbers when "translated" back into words using the above key give us TABLES and ABLEST.

The same exercise can be carried out with STRIPE, TRIPES and RIPEST where:

STRIPE = 1 x 142,857 = 142,857
TRIPES = 3 x 142,857 = 428,571
RIPEST = 2 x 142,857 = 285,714

To ponder...

What do the following words have in common? (**Question X**):

networker
sleightful
abstentionist
feminineness
xylophones

Go to page 217 if you need any help.

24
REVERSALS AND PALINDROMES

It comes as it goes

Our fascination with doing things backwards perhaps originates in our child-hood games. It is certainly an aspect which consumes a great deal of recreational energy judging by the occurrences of word and number games and puzzles from Roman times through to Victorian times and the present day with books and films such as Martin Amis' novel, *Time's Arrow*, and Christopher Nolan's film, *Memento*.

A palindrome is a word or sentence which reads the same backwards as it does forwards and comes from the Greek *palindromos* (*palin*, back again, and *dramen*, to run). Palindromes constitute a particular (elevated) form of reversal.

Palindromes in numbers

Reversals and palindromes extend also to numbers and number play.

What is a palindromic number? It is any number which reads the same starting from the right as it does from the left so that the digits 1 to 9 are each palin-dromic numbers as are numbers such as 111, 121, 14,641 and 1,367,631.

Here are some examples of number palindromes and reversals:

- 10,989 multiplied by 9 = 98,901

- 10,989 divided by the palindrome 99 generates another palindrome, 111. Similarly, 98,901 divided by 99 equals 999

- 1,089 multiplied by 9 = 9,801

- $111,111^2 = 12,345,654,321$

- $12^2 = 144$ and
  $21^2 = 441$

- $13^3 = 169$ and
  $31^2 = 961$

- $9 + 9 = 18$ and
  $9 \times 9 = 81$

- $2 + 497 = 499$ and
  $2 \times 497 = 994$

1980	9108
0891 -	8019 -
————	————
1089	1089

2178 x	4356 x
4	1.5
————	————
8712	6534

- 312 x   213 x
  221   while   122
  ————   ————
  68952   25986 – each a reversal of the other.

[Ball and Coxeter, *Mathematical Recreations and Essays*; Dover, 1987]

Take the number which is constituted by any four **consecutive** digits. Deduct from that number its reversal. For example:

4321 -
1234
_____

3087
======

3,087 will always be the result whatever four consecutive digits are chosen.

- A similar process (called Kaprekar's process) involves taking **any** number with four digits and rearranging them to form the largest possible number. The next step is to deduct from it the smallest number which can be formed from those four digits.

If the result is not 6,174 then repeat the process using the same digits until 6,174 is reached.

Example:

Take the four digits 3,7,7,1. The highest number which can be found by rearranging those digits is 7,731 and the lowest is 1,377.

Deducting the second of these from the first produces:

7731 -
1377
_____

6354
======

Repeat the process using the same digits 6, 3, 5 and 4:

6543 -
3456
_____

3087
======

and again...

8730 -
 378
_____

8352
======

and once again...

8532 –
2358
———
6174
===

It has taken four subtractions to reach 6,174. Some numbers take much more iterations, but eventually 6,174 will be reached whichever four digits we start with.

- Take any number and add it to its reversal. If the result does not generate a palindrome then repeat the exercise until it does.

For example:

192
291
———
483
384
———
867
768
———
1635
5361
———
6996
===

Most numbers will eventually yield a palindrome as a result of this process. However, recreational mathematicians have spent thousands of hours of computer time determining just which numbers (referred to as Lychrel numbers) are unlikely to produce a palindrome.

So far, it appears that any three-digit number with 9 in the middle and whose two outside digits add up to 7 may well be a Lychrel number including 196, 295 and 394 – although whether any particular number constitutes a Lychrel number is yet to be finally proved because the process of reversal and addition can carry on indefinitely and might, with any particular number, eventually generate a palindrome. 10,911, for example, takes 55 iterations before it produces a palindrome and so proves itself to be a non-Lychrel number. By contrast, 56 takes just one reversal: 56 + 65 = 121.

- Take any three-digit number where the first is greater than the last. As a first step, deduct its reversal to produce another number and, as a second step, add the reversal of that number. We always get the same result:

	Example 1	**Example 2**
Step 1: Start with	624 -	170 -
Step 2: Reverse it	426	071
	———	———
Step 3: Subtract	198 +	099 +
Step 4: Reverse it	891	990
	———	———
Step 5: Add steps 3 and 4	**1089**	**1089**

The answer will always be 1,089. Why this should be is explained on page 223.

Word palindromes and anagrams

Amongst the best well-known word palindromes are:

"Able was I ere I saw Elba" and

"A man, a plan, a canal – Panama"   [Leigh Mercer]

Two of the supposedly longest single-word palindromes are the 11-letter word *detartrated* and the nine-letter word *redivider* although neither appears in the OED.

Each of the above examples consists of the **letters** of the phrase reading the same both forwards and backwards. Phrasal palindromes may also be constructed by taking each **word** in the phrase and reading them both forwards and backwards as in:

"Much as girls dislike boys; few boys dislike girls as much."

An anagram (derived from the GK *ana-* and *gramma*, letter) is a word formed by transposing or jumbling up the letters of another word. So *mahogany* is an anagram of *hogmanay* and *consumerist* is an anagram of *misconstrue*.

The term *anagram* is sometimes used in a narrow sense to indicate a transposal which gives rise to a new word which has a resonance with the original (for example, *decorate* and *recoated* or *intoxicate* and *excitation*). Although that is too restrictive a definition and is not widely observed, the best anagrams are those where the original word is used to create a reordering of the letters of a word so as to produce some ironic or pithy relevance to it.

Some anagrams produce a result contradicting the original word, for example:

over fifty = forty-five
sixty-nine = ninety-six
funeral = real fun
honestly = on the sly
antagonist = not against
untied = united

Others might be thought to **endorse** the original word as in:

caviare = avarice
desperation = a rope ends it
decimal point = I'm a dot in place
astronomers = moon starers
soft-heartedness = often sheds tears
William Shakespeare = we all make his praise
Margaret Thatcher = that great charmer
Theresa May = she may rate
the eyes = they see

Some words spawn multiple anagrams. *Pears*, for example, is an anagram of *apers, asper, après, pares, parse, rapes, reaps, spare, spear, prase* and *presa*.

Here are some anagrams of numbers:

One: eon (an indeterminate period)
Two: owt (anything) tow, wot (form of what)
Three: ether, there
Seven: evens, neves (backslang)
Eleven: enleve (Ob to raise in relief)
Sixteen: extines (membrane of grain)
Three/ten: Ethernet (local area computer network)
Four/ten: fortune
Eight/ten: teething

Enormous effort must have gone into the following anagram (by Cory Calhoun) of the sentence in Shakespeare's *Hamlet*:

"To be or not to be: that is the question, whether tis nobler in the mind to suffer the slings and arrows of outrageous fortune."

– which metamorphoses into:

"In one of the Bard's best-thought-of tragedies, our insistent hero, Hamlet, queries on two fronts about how life turns rotten."

Dudeney

A well-known anagram devised by Henry Dudeney merely consists of adding one to twelve. Quite bizarrely, this equation, whether expressed in numbers or in words, constitutes an anagram:

(1 + 12) is an anagram of **(2 + 11)**

– and, in parallel:

one plus twelve is an anagram of **two plus eleven**

If that were not bizarre enough, each of these four equations adds up to 13.

To ponder…

Question Y: What do the following have in common?

Marxism
Leninism
Venetian
Genevese
Huguenot

Clue: Look for hidden words.

See page 217 for the answers.

25
ALL THE LETTERS AND ALL THE NUMBERS

Pangrams

Wordplay delights in the quest to find as plausible a sentence as possible utilising all 26 letters of the alphabet once only. Such a sentence, referred to as a pangram, is difficult to construct and although there have been many tries, none of them appears to have reached perfection.

The well-known typing test, slightly altered, provides us with the best-known pangram:

THE QUICK BROWN FOX JUMPS OVER A LAZY DOG

However, this is by no means a perfect example since it contains 33 letters with 2 **A**s, 2 **E**s, 4 **O**s, 2 **R**s and 2 **U**s.

Much effort has been expended to find a better example in the English language but the task has proved elusive where the goal is to avoid initials, foreign words, proper names and abbreviations at the same time as to produce a plausible grammatical sentence. The difficulty can be illustrated by the fact that perhaps the nearest pangram to achieve these ends is:

PACK MY BOX WITH FIVE DOZEN LIQUOR JUGS
– which uses only 32 letters.

Remarkably, an industrious researcher has gone to the length of ascertaining that Shakespeare's Sonnet 27 contains all 26 letters of the alphabet. Did Shakespeare set out to achieve that end? We may never know. However, the original order of the 154 sonnets is not known and possibly the order we currently observe is out by one so that Sonnet 27 might originally have been Sonnet 26. The first and last lines of this sonnet provide a tantalising clue to the truth: "Weary with toil…" and "…no quiet find" could well have presaged the sterling endeavours of that researcher.

Using all the digits

Recreational maths indulges in the same discipline by creating mathematical equations which utilise all the digits 1 to 9 (or sometimes 0 to 9).

Here are some examples:

- The number 5,346 has two sets of factors, the representations of which each use all the digits from 1 to 9:

  $18 \times 297 \quad = \quad 5{,}346$ and
  $27 \times 198 \quad = \quad 5{,}346$

- $4 \times 1{,}738 \quad = \quad 6{,}952$
  $4 \times 1{,}963 \quad = \quad 7{,}852$
  $28 \times 157 \quad = \quad 4{,}396$
  $42 \times 138 \quad = \quad 5{,}796$

  [Kordemsky, *The Moscow Puzzles*; Penguin, 1990]

- $9 \times 26 \times 531{,}487 \quad = \quad 124{,}367{,}958$ and
  $627 \times 198{,}354 \quad = \quad 124{,}367{,}958$

  [Madachy, FF, *Madachy's Mathematical Recreations*; Dover, 1979]

- $1 + 2 + 3 + 4 + 5 + 6 + 7 + [8 \times 9] \qquad = \quad 100$
  $1 + [2 \times 3] + [4 \times 5] - 6 + 7 + [8 \times 9] \qquad = \quad 100$
  $1 + [2 \times 3] + 4 + 5 + 67 + 8 + 9 \qquad = \quad 100$
  $12 + 3 - 4 + 5 + 67 + 8 + 9 \qquad = \quad 100$
  $12 - 3 - 4 + 5 - 6 + 7 + 89 \qquad = \quad 100$
  $123 + 4 - 5 + 67 - 89 \qquad = \quad 100$
  $123 - 45 - 67 + 89 \qquad = \quad 100$
  $123 - 4 - 5 - 6 - 7 + 8 - 9 \qquad = \quad 100$
  $[1 + 2 - 3 - 4] \times [5 - 6 - 7 - 8 - 9] \qquad = \quad 100$
  $1^{23} + 4 + 5 - 6 + 7 + 89 \qquad = \quad 100$
  $[1 \times 2] + 3^4 - 5 - 67 + 89 \qquad = \quad 100$

- 98 - 76 + 54 + 3 + 21   =   100

- 50 ½ + 49 $^{38}/_{76}$ =   100

- $\dfrac{148}{296} + \dfrac{35}{70}$ =   1

- The smallest number which is a square using only all nine digits is 139,854,276 = $11,826^2$ and the largest number utilising all the nine digits which is a square is 923,187,456 the square root of which is 30,384.
  [Beiler, *Recreations in Theory of Numbers*; Dover, 1966]

- 987,654,321 minus 123,456,789 equals 864,197,532 which again utilises all the digits from 1 to 9 once only.
  [Wells, *The Penguin Dictionary of Curious and Interesting Numbers*; Penguin,1988]

- 123,456,789, when multiplied in turn by 2, 4, 5, 7 and 8, will in each case produce an "anagram" of itself:

  123,456,789 x 2 = 246,913,578
  123,456,789 x 4 = 493,827,156
  123,456,789 x 5 = 617,283,945
  123,456,789 x 7 = 864,197,523
  123,456,789 x 8 = 987,654,312

- 987,654,321 when multiplied in turn by 2, 4, 5, 7 and 8 also produces an "anagram" with a zero added in each case for completeness.

  987,654,321 x 2 = 1,975,308,642
  987,654,321 x 4 = 3,950,617,284
  987,654,321 x 5 = 4,938,271,605
  987,654,321 x 7 = 6,913,580,247
  987,654,321 x 8 = 7,901,234,568

- Interesting results arise when the 8 is excluded:

  12,345,679 x 8 = 98,765,432 (the 8 returns but the 1 goes missing)
  12,345,679 x 2 = 24,691,358 (7 is missing)
  12,345,679 x 4 = 49,382,716 (5 is missing)
  12,345,679 x 5 = 61,728,395 (4 is missing)
  12,345,679 x 7 = 86,419,753 (2 is missing)

In each case, the aggregate of the multiplier and the missing digit comes to 9.

- We see from the preceding example that 12,345,679 x 7 = 86,419,753 where the number 2 is missing...and here it is: 123,456,789 x 7 = 864,197,523.

- 111,111,111 x 111,111,111 = 12,345,678,987,654,321

26
FIBONACCI SEQUENCE

Leonardo of Pisa

If you were to take 1 and 1 as the first two numbers of a sequence and add them together to create 2 as the next number in that sequence you would be well on the way to producing that most intriguing series of numbers, created by Leonardo of Pisa, the renowned thirteenth-century Italian mathematician who, after his death in Pisa in 1250, became known as Fibonacci.

So, add 1 and 1 = 2 and take the 2 as the third term to produce **1, 1, and 2**. Repeat the exercise by adding 1 to 2 = 3 to produce the extended sequence **1, 1, 2, 3**. The last two numbers of this new sequence when added together make 5 and this is added to create the new sequence of **1, 1, 2, 3, 5**. The process can be carried on indefinitely. In each case, adding the last two numbers in the sequence gives the next number. Hence, the first 18 numbers in the Fibonacci sequence are:

1, 1, 2, 3, 5, 8, 13, 21, 34, 55, 89, 144, 233, 377, 610, 987, 1,597 and **2,584.**

This sequence is one of the most famous in mathematics, having scores of applications in mathematical analysis, and is remarkable for the instances in which it occurs in nature in many different guises. The contribution of Alan Turing (the Bletchley Park code-breaker during World War II) in developing research into this phenomenon has recently been acknowledged by the Museum of Science and Industry in Manchester.

There are many examples in nature where, for some inexplicable reason, numbers in the Fibonacci sequence occur in the patterns created by plants. For example, the numbers of the cells on the spirals found on the outside of a pineapple or a pinecone are invariably Fibonacci numbers and the number of petals typically found on many flowers happens to be a Fibonacci number. There are often 5 petals on a buttercup, 8 on delphiniums, 13 on the ragwort, and 21 on asters. Daisies are often found with 34, 55 or 89 petals and sunflowers with 3, 5, 8, 13, 21, 34 or 55. The growth of a nautilus shell also seems to have properties reminiscent of the Fibonacci sequence.

If we wanted to work out the number of the pairs of rabbits which would be produced starting with a single pair of rabbits where, in every month, each pair bears a new pair which becomes productive from the second month, then we need only refer to the Fibonacci sequence to find the answer.

The sequence has inspired musicians and poets and, most famously, architects. If we take each successive Fibonacci number starting with 5 and divide it by the previous number in the series we get an interesting result. The number produced is approximately 1.6. From 233 onwards the number created by that process is 1.618. So, for example, $233/144 = 1.618$. This is recognisable as the Golden Ratio much admired by the Greeks and, in particular, by their architects and known as Phi or Ø which approximates to 1.618033989. Interestingly, 1 divided by 1.618033989 is equal to 0.618033989 (the reciprocal of Phi) or Phi minus 1.

Another way of arriving at Phi is by the simple formula **$(1+\sqrt{5})/2$** which equals 1.618033989. The Greeks called this number the Golden Ratio since the ratio of 1:1.618033989 produces a most aesthetically pleasing proportion which was adopted widely in Greek architecture, art and design to create harmony and balance. The proportions of the Parthenon, for example, are based on Phi. Da Vinci's *Mona Lisa* perhaps enthrals us the more because her face is in this proportion. Le Corbusier employed the Golden Ratio in his designs.

If we want an everyday example of what the ratio looks like, we need to look no further than the standard credit card. ISO, the International Organization for Standardization, has set the dimensions for most ID cards and credit cards (ISO/IEC 7810:2003) at 85.60 cms x 53.98 cms. Now, 85.60 divided by 53.98 is not far short of Phi. If the longer side were just 1.7414747262 centimetres longer (that is, 87.3414747262 cms), the standard credit card would be a near perfect example of the Golden Ratio.

So prevalent is the Fibonacci sequence that we can find it occurring in other unexpected places. Let us take the tedious task of sticking stamps onto envelopes where we have only £1 and £2 stamps. How many different ways are there to affix stamps for successive postage costs starting at £1 taking each combination of £1 and £2 stamps as different? (Affixing a £1 stamp and then a £2 stamp is thus to be treated as an alternative to affixing a £2 stamp first and then a £1 stamp.)

The surprising number of alternatives is shown as follows:

Total value of postage stamps required:	Order of affixing stamps: 1 = £1 and 2 = £2	Number of alternative methods:
£1	1	1
£2	11 or 2	2
£3	111 or 12 or 21	3
£4	1111 or 22 or 211 or 121 or 112	5
£5	11111 or 221 or 212 or 122 or 1112 or 2111 or 1211 or 1121	8
£6	111111 or 222 or 1122 or 1212 or 1221 or 11112 or 21111 or 12111 or 11211 or 11121 or 2211 or 2112 or 2121	13

Fig. 1

Each successive £1 of value produces a result found by adding the two previous results together in the same way as in the Fibonacci sequence.

The Fibonacci sequence provides a treasure trove of fascinating mathematical connections far too complex for this tome. The following are just two examples.

Consecutive Fibonacci numbers

Take any four consecutive Fibonacci numbers. The square of the third (that is multiplying it by itself) minus the square of the second, when divided by the first, will always give us the fourth. Here is an example taking **5**, **8**, **13** and **21**:

$$13^2 = 169 >> 169 - 8^2 = 105 >> {}^{105}/_5 = 21$$

Fibonacci party trick

The Fibonacci sequence can be harnessed to develop an effective party trick.

Ask a volunteer to create his own six-digit long Fibonacci sequence, firstly by selecting **any** two numbers less than 20 and extending that sequence to six numbers by adding (in the same way as Fibonacci does) the last two numbers in the sequence to find the next. If, for example, the volunteer chooses 7 and 13 as the first two numbers in his sequence then the next four will be 20, 33, 53 and 86 to create a Fibonacci-like sequence of six numbers: **7**, **13**, **20**, **33**, **53** and **86**.

Request that the volunteer writes down his sequence, stopping him after the fifth, at which point you write down a number (without showing it to him) which you predict will be equal to the addition of all of his **six** numbers. Your volunteer completes the sequence, adds up the six numbers and you compare your two sets of calculations to reveal your prowess.

The trick is very simple because the total of the first six numbers in any Fibonacci-like sequence will always be equal to four times the fifth. Here the total of the above six numbers comes to 212 which is equal to 4 x **53**, the fifth in the sequence. The fact that this works even though the first two numbers are chosen at random makes the trick even more appealing.

You may chance your arm further by getting your volunteer to extend his sequence by another four numbers:

7, **13**, **20**, **33**, **53**, **86**, **139**, **225**, **364** and **589**

You will be able to announce the aggregate value of these ten numbers immediately after you determine the seventh because that aggregate will always be 11 times the seventh number of the sequence, that is, here 11 x **139** = 1,529. Assistance in multiplying by 11, in your head, is given in Chapter 11. The mathematical explanation of this party trick is set out on page 218: **Question Z**.

Fibs

The attraction of the Fibonacci sequence is not reserved for mathematicians; it extends also to wordsmiths. A screenwriter in Los Angeles, Gregory Pincus, invited his blog aficionados to create six-line verses (called Fibs) which follow the pattern of having a single syllable word in the first two lines, two in the third line, three in the fourth, five in the fifth and eight in the last line. That is lines of 1,1, 2, 3, 5 and 8 syllables, being the first six numbers of the Fibonacci sequence.

The idea has been popular. Here is my offering:

One
One
Arrive.
Leads to two
Then three and to five,
Eight being the next we derive.

The task can become addictive.

ANSWERS: A TO Z

Page 21

Question A

The time and date consists exclusively of odd numbers and (taking zero as an even number) this will not occur at any time between those two dates which are separated by just over 1,111 years.

Page 22

Question B

Both express the time and date exclusively in even numbers. Amazingly, the gap between the two dates is the same as in Question A – 1,111 years.

Question C

It can be seen that the phrase "never odd or even " (as well as the phrase "never ever even") are palindromes reading the same backwards as they do forwards. See Chapter 24 for Reversals and Palindromes. The mathematician's preferred answer may well be that numbers expressed as fractions or as decimals can never be treated as odd or even.

Page 30

Question D

6, 3, 2. The sequence constitutes the numbers one to nine in alphabetical order.

Page 31

Question E

89, 97, 102. Each of these numbers when expressed as a word begins with the same letter as it ends with.

Question F

3, 5. The sequence is the number of letters in each of the numbers one to nine.

Question G

36 and 30. The sequence takes the numbers one to ten and is arrived at by multiplying each successive number by the number of letters occurring in it so that the first in the sequence, one, has three letters and 1 x 3 = 3.

Page 32

Question H

E, N, T. They are the first letters of each of the numbers two to ten.

Question I

S, S for sixthly, seventhly.

Question J

In many English dictionaries, the next entry will be "dish".

Question K

On a 24-hour digital clock displaying seconds as well as hours and minutes, these two times will be the only times each day which will show a sequence of six consecutive digits, namely, 01:23:45 and 12:34:56.

[Thanks to David Kersey of Kent and *The Times*]

Page 54

Question L

Some possible words using the letters I, E, H, S, G, L, B and O:

BEIGELS	5736138
BELLIES	5317738
BLESSES	5355378
BOBSLEIGHS	5461375808
BOGGLES	5376608
BOLSHIE	3145708
BOOGIES	5316008
EGGSHELLS	577345663
GIGOLOS	5070616
GHILLIES	53177146
GLOSSLESS	553755076
GOBBLES	5378806

GOOGLES	5376006
HELLISH	4517734
HILLBILLIES	53177187714
HOBBIES	5318804
HOBBLES	5378804
ILLEGIBLE	378163771
LEGLESS	5537637
OBLIGES	5361780
OBSESSES	53553580
SHOELESS	55373045
SHELL-HOLES	53704-77345

Page 55
Question M

Everyone assumed that the list was headed 6 NOS and that the numbers add up to 5661 whereas the sheet of paper was held the wrong way up. If viewed the other way up, with the signature SON 9, the six numbers add up to 4590.

Page 57
Question N

TABLES	142857
x E	x 5
STABLES	714285

Question O

ONE	984
+ NINE	+ 8584
+ FIFTY	+ 75732
+ TWENTY	+ 364832
= EIGHTY	+ 450132

ONE	621
+ TWO	+ 846
+ FIVE	+ 9071
= EIGHT	= 10538

[M. Brooke, *150 Puzzles in Crypt-Arithmetic*; Dover, 1969]

SEVEN	68782
+ SEVEN	+ 68782
+ SIX	+ 650
= TWENTY	= 138214

[M. Brooke, *150 Puzzles in Crypt-Arithmetic*; Dover, 1969]

```
        MAUVE            72508
      + RUSSET         + 654483
      ─────────        ─────────
    = MAROON           = 726991
      ═════════        ═════════


         GREY             6892
      + YELLOW         + 294475
      ─────────        ─────────
      = INDIGO         = 301367
      ═════════        ═════════
```

Page 64

Question P

1,024,375,869.

Page 72

Question Q

A surprising method for working out the number of routes where one cell is "out of bounds" can be found if you have the two following matrices in front of you.

The first is Fig. 3 from page 71:

	A	**B**	**C**	**D**	**E**	*y*
1	1	5	15	35	70	
2	1	4	**10**	20	35	
3	1	3	6	10	15	
4	1	2	3	4	5	
5	1	1	1	1	1	

x

Fig. 3

The second is the same Fig. 3 rotated 180 degrees to create a new Fig. 6 as below:

	A	B	C	D	E
1	1	1	1	1	1
2	5	4	3	2	1
3	15	10	6	3	1
4	35	20	10	4	5
5	70	35	15	5	1

Fig. 6

In order to find the number of possible routes from x to y where one cell in Fig. 3 is blocked or "out of bounds", simply multiply the number appearing in that blocked cell (before you reduce it to zero) by the number appearing in the same numbered cell in Fig. 6 and deduct the result from 70. Hence, if the blocked cell in Fig. 3 is C2 (that is, **10**) multiply that 10 by the number in the same C2 cell in Fig.6 (that is, **3**) to get 30 and deduct 30 from 70 to get 40 which, indeed, is the number of routes available. (This also works with **two** blocked cells by aggregating the result of the multiplication exercise above for each blocked cell and deducting 70 but does not work when the blocked cell in Fig. 3 is one of those having a value of 1.)

Page 95
Question R

The six permutations of any three-digit number (xyz) are xyz, xzy, yxz, yzx, zyx and zxy. It can be seen from this that x, y and z each appear twice as hundreds, twice as tens and twice as units. Hence, the aggregate of the six permutations will be:

2 ($x+y+z$)	x 100
2 ($x+y+z$)	x 10
2 ($x+y+z$)	x 1

or **2 ($x+y+z$)**   **x 111**

Applying this equation to example 5 on page 95 gives us: 2 x (6 + 2 + 4) x 111 = **2,664**.

Pages 114 and 115
Question S

Rows

1	**O**
2	**OO**
3	**OO**
4	**OOO**
5	**OO**ooo

Fig. 2

If you are the player whose turn it is to move, you should take three coins from row 5 so as to leave:

2 x 1s (in rows 1 and 4) and
4 x 2s (in rows 2, 3, 4 and 5).

After this, there will be an **even** number of 1s and an **even** number of 2s thus rendering the position "safe". If your opponent's next move was, for example, to remove the one remaining coin in row 1, you would be able once again to render the position "safe" by taking one coin from row 4 leaving the requisite even number, namely, 4 x 2s.

Page 161
Question T

Row

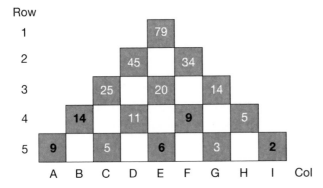

Fig. 3

Row

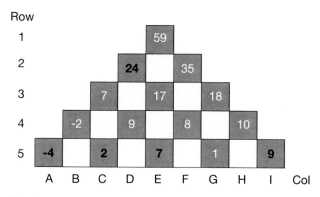

Fig. 4

Page 161
Question U and method

Row

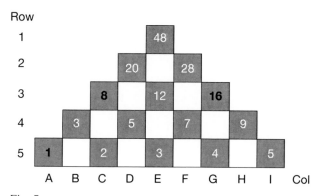

Fig. 5

One method for solving Fig. 5 on page 161 is as follows:

Starting with cell **3C** it will be apparent that this must be the result of adding the values in **5A** + 2(**5C**) + **5E**. (**5C** is counted twice since it figures both in cell **4B** and **4D**).

Since **5A** + 2(**5C**) + **5E** = 8 and **5A** = 1 there are only three possibilities:

5C = 1 and **5E** = 5; or
5C = 2 and **5E** = 3; or
5C = 3 and **5E** = 1.

Since **5A** has already been allocated the value 1, neither **5C** nor **5E** can equal 1 so that **5C** must equal 2 and **5E** equals 3 which enables us also to complete cells **4B** and **4D**.

Moving to cell **3G**, this must have the value of $5E + 2(5G) + 5I$. Since $5E + 2(5G) + 5I = 16$ and $5E = 3$, it follows that $2(5G) + 5I = 13$ which leaves us with two possibilities:

$5G = 4$ and cell $5I = 5$; or
$5G = 5$ and cell $5I = 3$.

But cell **5E** has already been allocated the value of 3 so that **5G** must equal 4 and **5I** must equal 5. Since we have the values for each of the cells in row 5 this enables us to complete the entries in the rest of the pyramid in the normal way and to arrive at the value of 48 in cell **1E**.

Page 164
Question V

ROW	SEQUENCE
1	1
2	11
3	21
4	1211
5	111221
6	312211
7	13112221
8	1113213211

Fig. 8

Row 1 starts with number 1 and row 2 describes it as consisting of "one one" or "11"

Row 3 describes row 2 as consisting of "two ones" or "21".

Row 4 describes row 3 as "one two and one one" or "1211" and so on.

Page 176
Answers to Dingbats®

Newcastle-under-Lyme

A gross injustice

Potatoes

Scrambled eggs

On horseback

Overwhelming odds

Water (H_2O)

A mixed metaphor

Made in China

You take after your mother

Page 179
Question W
"Humpty Dumpty sat on a wall..."

Page 189
Question X
Each of the five words contains a hidden number within its confines and one which is not pronounced in the same way as it is pronounced as a standalone number.

Page 197
Question Y
Each word contains the letters of a number written backwards.

Page 206

Question Z

Why is the aggregate of the first six numbers in any Fibonacci sequence always equal to the fifth number in that sequence?

Expressing the first ten terms in the sequence in algebraic terms as follows, with x as the first term and y as the second, will reveal why:

Fibonacci number	Position of number	Algebraic value of each number	Algebraic value of cumulative total	Cumulative value	Equivalence
1	1st	x	x	1	
1	2nd	y	$x + y$	2	
2	3rd	$x + y$	$2x + 2y$	4	
3	4th	$x + 2y$	$3x + 4y$	7	
5	5th	$2x + 3y$	$5x + 7y$	12	
8	6th	$3x + 5y$	$8x + 12y$	20	Equal to 4 x 5th No.
13	7th	$5x + 8y$	$13x + 20y$	33	
21	8th	$8x + 13y$	$21x + 33y$	54	
34	9th	$13x + 21y$	$34x + 54y$	88	
55	10th	$21x + 34y$	$55x + 88y$	143	Equal to 11 x 7th No.

Fig. 2

The fifth term in the sequence is $2x + 3y$ and the aggregate of the first to the sixth terms comes to $8x + 12y$ which is four times the value of the fifth term.
[Thanks to Malcolm Levene]

Similarly, the seventh term is $5x + 8y$ which, when multiplied by 11, equals the aggregate of the first ten terms, namely, $55x + 88y$.

These equivalences apply whether or not the sequence begins with the two numbers 1 and 1 and whether or not the first such number is greater than the second. The first two numbers can even include fractions or decimal points. All that is required is that the series follows the Fibonacci rule that the third and each successive number in the series is the result of adding the two previous numbers in that series.

PROOFS AND EXPLANATIONS

Pages 77 and 107

Some cyclic numbers

Two interesting cyclic numbers are 142,857 and the 18-digit number 526,315,789,473,684,210 [from *Figuring, The Joy of Numbers* by Shakuntala Devi; Andre Deutsch, 1977]

When 142,857 is multiplied by 2, 3, 4, 5 or 6 the product consists of the same six digits in the same order but commencing on each occasion from a different starting point within the string:

1	multiplied by	142,857	=	142,857
2	multiplied by	142,857	=	285,714
3	multiplied by	142,857	=	428,571
4	multiplied by	142,857	=	571,428
5	multiplied by	142,857	=	714,285
6	multiplied by	142,857	=	857,142
7	multiplied by	142,857	=	999,999
8	multiplied by	142,857	=	1,142,856
9	multiplied by	142,857	=	1,285,713
10	multiplied by	142,857	=	1,428,570
11	multiplied by	142,857	=	1,571,427
12	multiplied by	142,857	=	1,714,284
13	multiplied by	142,857	=	1,857,141
14	multiplied by	142,857	=	1,999,998
15	multiplied by	142,857	=	2,142,855

It will be seen that 142,857 multiplied by 7 equals 999,999.

Multiplying 142,857 by any number which is a multiple of 7 will, with a little prestidigitation (that is by adding together the opening and closing digits of each result) also produce a row of 9s. The key is that 1 divided by 7 (the reciprocal of 7) is equal to 0.142857.

A similar effect is produced when we find the reciprocal of 13 and play with the number 76,923.

526,315,789,473,684,210 produces similar results where the appropriate starting point is the reciprocal of 19.

Page 96
Proof of adding/multiplication puzzle

$$\frac{x}{x-1}$$

1) **adding** this fraction to x we get:

$$\frac{x}{x-1} + \frac{x}{1} = \frac{x}{x-1} + \frac{x(x-1)}{x-1}$$

$$= \frac{x + x^2 - x}{x-1} = \frac{x^2}{x-1}$$

2) **multiplying** this fraction by x we get:

$$\frac{x}{x-1} \times \frac{x}{1} = \frac{x^2}{x-1}$$

Hence, each of these processes gives rise to the same result thus proving that:

$$\frac{x}{x-1} \text{ plus } x$$

is equal to:

$$\frac{x}{x-1} \text{ multiplied by } x$$

Explanation of Russian multiplication

Behind the simple process of Russian multiplication described in Chapter 11 is a complex series of procedures. Let us examine these by reference to a simple example where we wish to multiply 10 by 9 using Russian multiplication.

Step 1: Having entered 10 in column 1 (instead of the figure 97 in Fig. 3 on page 97) we proceed to halve 10 and enter the result in the row below. We then halve the result of each successive halving in column 1 until we get to 1.

The hidden effect of this process is to create a binary (or base 2) equivalent of 10 (see Chapter 12). This can be found by taking the remainder resulting from each halving (which will obviously be 0 or 1) and reading those remainders from the bottom to the top to form a number. So:

Column 1					Remainder column
10	divided by 2	equals	5	with remainder	0
5	divided by 2	equals	2	with remainder	1
2	divided by 2	equals	1	with remainder	0
1	divided by 2	equals	0	with remainder	1
			1 0 1 0		

Reading from the bottom up in the remainder column we get **1010**.

Step 2: 1 0 1 0 in binary form can be "translated" into decimal as follows:

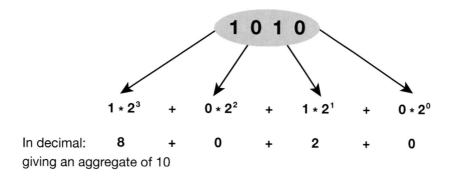

$$1 * 2^3 \quad + \quad 0 * 2^2 \quad + \quad 1 * 2^1 \quad + \quad 0 * 2^0$$

In decimal: 8 + 0 + 2 + 0
giving an aggregate of 10

$0 * 2^2$ and $0 * 2^0$ above both equal zero and can therefore be ignored or deleted (as can the four deleted lines in Fig. 3 on page 97) so as to leave us with number 10 represented merely by **$(1 * 2^3) + (1 * 2^1)$**. (Steps 1 and 2 when applied to **any** number will generate that number.)

Step 3: Having reformulated 10 in this way, first by the halving process and then by the deletion process so as to generate **(1 * 2^3) + (1 * 2^1)**, we can now move to the next stage, namely, to multiply this new formulation of 10 by number 9 which is entered in column 2. However, instead of multiplying the **whole** number by 9, we multiply each of its two **elements** by 9 giving the same result.

Applying this process thus gives us:

(9 * 2^3) + (9 * 2^1)

This part of the process can be done by successive doubling. This is because multiplying any number by 2 (or 2^1) can be achieved merely by doubling that number and multiplying any number by 2^3 involves doubling three times so that:

(9 * 2^3) = 72 (9 successively doubled three times: 18, 36 >> **72**) and

(9 * 2^1) = 18 (9 doubled once >> **18**)

This explains the function of the doubling process that we apply in column 2 of Fig. 2 on page 97.

Step 4: The final step is the same as the final step in our example in Fig. 3 on page 97, namely, to add the 72 and the 18 in step 3 to reach 90 being the answer we are expecting.

If we multiply 10 by 9 using Russian multiplication we can, in summary, see how all the above steps are so effectively conflated as follows:

Column 1	Column 2
halving	doubling
10	9
5	18
2	36
1	72
	90

It is remarkable how the four complex steps above are effectively implemented by such a simple process requiring just seven straightforward entries.

Page 195

Proof of 1,089 puzzle

The following steps use algebra to represent the five steps on page 195:

Step 1: We start with a three-digit number (abc): $100a + 10b + c$.

Step 2: Reversing the three digits in step 1 gives us: $100c + 10b + a$.

Step 3: Deducting the number at step 2 from that at step 1 gives: $99a - 99c$.

This shows that the result of this process (let us call it xyz) must be divisible by 99. In every such three-digit number, xyz, which is exactly divisible by 99, y must equal 9 and $x + z$ must also equal 9. This enables us to reconfigure the result at step 3 and to express it instead as: $100x + 90 + (9 - x)$.

Step 4: We now reverse this reconfigured number to give us: $100(9 - x) + 90 + x$.

Step 5: Adding these together we get: $100x + 90 + (9 - x) + 100(9 - x) + 90 + x$. Which when simplified $= 100x + 90 + 9 - x + 900 - 100x + 90 + x$. All the xs cancel out to leave $= 90 + 9 + 900 + 90 = \mathbf{1,089}$.

GLOSSARY

Alphametic

A puzzle in which letters of the **alpha**bet (often formed so as to make some plausible phrase) are replaced by digits to create a working arith**metic** calculation.

Base

The basis of a particular number system so that, for example, the decimal system is based on the digits 0 to 9 whereas the binary system is based merely on the digits 0 and 1.

Checksum

A sum computed by reference to a set of digits which can later be used to check the correctness of that set.

Cognate

Words are said to be cognate with each other if they are both descendants of another word in an ancestral language and thus related.

Cube

A number multiplied by itself twice so that 4 cubed (written as 4^3 and referred to as "x to the power 3") is 64 where 4 appears three times in the calculation. The cube root of a number is that number which, when multiplied by itself twice, produces the original number, so that the cube root of 125 is 5.

Cyclic number

An integer having n digits which when multiplied by successive numbers from 1 to n results in a product with the same n digits in a cyclic order, as in 142,857.

Equation

A mathematical statement indicating that two different expressions have the same value or are equal as in the statement that $4 + 5 = 9$ or $x - y = z$.

Factor
Any whole number which divides exactly into another.

Factorial
In relation to any integer, factorial indicates the result of multiplying, in turn, each of the numbers from 1 up to and including that number, so that factorial 4 (or 4!) is equal to 4 x 3 x 2 x 1 (or 24) where the number of items to be multiplied is four.

Homophone
One of a set of words which sound the same but which have different meanings or spellings.

Integer
Any whole number including a negative number (and also zero).

Intransitive
See **Transitive/Intransitive** below.

Multiplier and Multiplicand
In multiplication, the number which is multiplied is called the *multiplicand* and the number by which it is multiplied is the *multiplier*. The result is the *product*.

Power
As regards any number, indicates how many of that given number are to be multiplied together so that "3 to the power 4" (strictly, "3 to the *exponent* 4") (or 3^4) equals 3 x 3 x 3 x 3 or 81 where 3 occurs in the calculation four times.

Prime
A whole number is referred to as *prime* if its factors (the numbers which divide into it without a remainder) consist merely of 1 and itself. 19 is a prime number, for example, because no numbers other than 1 and 19 divide into it without a remainder.

Product
See **Multiplier and Multiplicand** above.

Reciprocal
The reciprocal of any number is 1 divided by that number. The reciprocal of 8 is thus ⅛ or one-eighth or 0.125. The reciprocal of a fraction is the inverse of that fraction so that the reciprocal of ½ is ²⁄₁ or 2.

Remainder

That which is left after dividing one whole number by another. The result, for example, of dividing 15 by 2 can be expressed as 7 with remainder 1.

Short scale and Long scale

As regards recording numbers of an order of magnitude of 1,000,000,000 or more, the short scale is the method in which every such order is one thousand times larger than the previous. In the long scale, every step is one million times larger than the previous order.

Square and Square root

When a number is multiplied by itself once the product is referred to as the square of that number. Thus, 5 squared is 25. The square of x is written as x^2 (referred to as "x to the power 2") where 2 appears twice in the calculation. The square root of a number is such number as when multiplied by itself produces the original number so that the square root of 25 is 5.

Transitive/Intransitive

In the phrase "he eats lunch" the verb *eats* is said to be transitive since there is an object, namely, *lunch*. Whereas in the phrase "he eats quickly" there is no object and the verb is treated as being intransitive. Many verbs – such as *to appear, to laugh, to erupt* and *to sneeze* – have no object and are thus always intransitive.

BIBLIOGRAPHY

Author's Note: It occurs to me that this book has been in preparation over a much longer period than I had originally assumed, a lot of the entries having their source in material which I picked up while I was a teenager. I have also, during the process, drawn heavily on many of the following books which have inspired me in one way or another. It is both by way of acknowledgement to them and a desire to inspire others that I set out this lengthy list of sources.

AUTHOR	TITLE	PUBLISHER	YEAR
Abdelnoor, R E Jason	Mathematical Dictionary, A	Nelson	1989
Abrahams, R M	Diversions & Pastimes	Constable & Co	1933
Abrahams, Roger D & Rankin, Lois	Dictionary of Counting-Out Games, A	University of Texas Press	1980
Abrams, M H	Glossary of Literary Terms (5th ed.)	Holt Rinehart Winston	1985
Adams, Morley	Puzzle Book	Faber & Faber	1939
Adams, Morley	Puzzle Parade	Faber	1948
Adler, Irving	Magic House of Numbers	Dennis Dobson	1957
Agostini, Franco	Intelligence Games	Guild	1987
Aitchison, James	Cassell's Dictionary of English Grammar	Cassell	1996
Aitchison, James	Cassell's Guide to Written English	Cassell	2001
Albertson, Ralph	Mental Agility Book – An Encyclopaedia of Educational Puzzles & Parlour Games	Albert & Charles Boni	1925
Alderton Pink, M	Dictionary of Correct English, A	Pitman & Sons	1929
Allardyce, Paul	STOPS or How to Punctuate	T Fisher Unwin	1902
Allen, R E	Oxford Writers Dictionary, The	OUP	1990
Allen, Robert (Ed.)	How to Write Better English	Penguin	2005
Allen, Robert (Ed.)	Penguin English Dictionary, The	Penguin	2002
Allhusen, Edward	Fopdoodle and Salmagundi – Words and Meanings from Dr Johnson's Dictionary That Time Forgot	Old House Books	2007
Anderson, Trevor (Ed.)	Chambers Encyclopaedia, The	Chambers Harrap	2001

Andrews, W S	Magic Squares and Cubes	Dover	1960
Annandale, Charles	New Gresham Dictionary of the English Language, The	Gresham	1930
Anonymous	Bingo Boys and Poodle-Fakers – A Curious Compendium of Historical Slang	The Folio Society	2007
Anonymous	Bloomsbury Thematic Dictionary of Quotations	Bloomsbury	1989
Anonymous	Business Terms, Phrases and Abbreviations	Pitman	1964
Anonymous	Chambers Words	Chambers	1982
Anonymous	Collins Clear Type Illustrated Pronouncing Dictionary	Collins	1900
Anonymous	Dictionary of Printing Terms, A	Linotype & Machinery	1962
Anonymous	Dictionary of Spelling	Hutchinson Pocket	1994
Anonymous	Dictionary of Unusual Words Part A	Thames Bank	1946
Anonymous	Dictionary of Unusual Words Part B	Thames Bank	1948
Anonymous	English/Cockney Rhyming Slang Dictionary	www	1997
Anonymous	Funk & Wagnalls Concise Standard Dictionary	Funk & Wagnalls	1959
Anonymous	Hart's Rules for Compositors and Readers	OUP	1983
Anonymous	Illustrated Dictionary of Unfamiliar Words	Robson Books	2000
Anonymous	Johnson's Dictionary – A New and Enlarged Dictionary of the English Language	Isaac, Tuckey and Co	1836
Anonymous	Lock Stock & Barrel	Past Times	1998
Anonymous	Longmans' Etymological and Biographical Dictionary	Longmans,Green	1928
Anonymous	Macmillan Dictionary of Contemporary Phrase & Fable	MacMillan	2002
Anonymous	Manual of Style, A (13th ed.)	Univ of Chicago	1982
Anonymous	Mazawattee Dictionary	Mazawattee	1911
Anonymous	Merriam Webster's Pocket Guide To Business and Everyday Math	Toppan Co (Singapore)	1996
Anonymous	New Encyclopaedia Britannica, The (16th ed.)	Encycl. Britannica	1983
Anonymous	New Illustrated Pronouncing Dictionary of the English Language	Collins	1890
Anonymous	New International Webster's Pocket Dictionary of The English Language, The	Webster	2002
Anonymous	Official Scrabble Players Dictionary, The (4th ed.)	Merriam-Webster	2005
Anonymous	Pig In The Poke, A	Grange Books	2003
Anonymous	Reader's Digest The Origins of Words & Phrases	Reader's Digest	?
Anonymous	Reuters Glossary of International Economic and Financial Terms	William Heinemann	1982
Anonymous	Salt of the Earth – Origins and Meanings of Country Sayings	National Trust Books	2002
Anonymous	Scrabble Lists, Official (2nd ed.)	Collins	2008

Anonymous	Slang Dictionary, The	Chatto & Windus	1925
Anonymous	Stroud's Judicial Dictionary	Sweet & Maxwell	1974
Anonymous	Style Book, The Guardian	The Guardian	1962?
Anonymous	Why Do We Say It? The Stories Behind the Words, Expressions and Cliches We Use	Castle Books	1985
Anonymous	Baffle Puzzles	Sphere Books	1983
Arncliffe, Thomas	Spelling of English, The	Eagle Press	1935
Augarde, Tony	Oxford Guide to Word Games, The	Oxford	1986
Augarde, Tony	Oxford Word Challenge	OUP	1998
Augarde, Tony	Oxford A to Z of Word Games, The	OUP	1994
Augarde, Tony	Oxford Guide to Word Games, The (revised ed.)	OUP	2003
Austin, J L	How To Do Things With Words	Oxford	1962
Austin, Tim	Times Guide to English Style and Usage, The	Times Books	1999
Austin, Tim	Times Style and Usage Guide, The	Times Books	2003
Ayto, John	Dictionary of Foreign Words in English	Wordsworth	1995
Ayto, John	Oxford Dictionary of Rhyming Slang	Oxford University Press	2003
Ayto, John	Euphemisms	Bloomsbury	1993
Ayto, John	Oxford Dictionary of Slang, The	Oxford	1998
Ayto, John	Dictionary of Word Origins	Columbia	1994
Ayto, John (Ed.)	Hutchinson Dictionary of Difficult Words	Hutchinson	1994
Bagnall, Nicholas	Defence of Clichés, A	Constable	1985
Bailey, Nathan	Universal Etymological English Dictionary, An	Charles Elliot	1789
Baldick, Chris	Concise Oxford Dictionary of Literary Terms, The	OUP	1990
Ball, W W R	Mathematical Recreations and Essays	MacMillan	1939
Barber, C L	Story of Language, The	Pan	1964
Barham, Andrea	Pedant's Revolt, The – Why Most Things You Think Are Right Are Wrong	Michael O'Mara Books	2005
Barnard, D St P	Figure It Out	Pan	1973
Barnard, D St P	It's All Done By Numbers	John Baker	1966
Barnett S, Berman M & Burto W	Dictionary of Literary Terms	Constable	1964
Barnett, Lincoln	Treasure of Our Tongue, The	Secker & Warburg	1966
Barnhart, CL & S & Steinmetz, S	Second Barnhart Dictionary of New English, The	Harper & Row	1980
Barnhart, Robert K, (Ed.)	Chambers Dictionary of Etymology (formerly The Barnhart Dictionary of Etymology)	Chambers	2000
Baron, Dennis	Grammar and Gender	Yale University	1986
Barr, Stephen	Man In The Milk Carton, The	Harper & Row	1990
Bath, Philip E	Fun With Words	Epworth Press	1959

Beard, H and Cerf, C	Official Politically Correct Dictionary and Handbook, The	Grafton	1992
Beasley, John D	Mathematics of Games, The	Oxford	1989
Beckson, Karl & Ganz, Arthur	Reader's Guide to Literary Terms, A	Thames & Hudson	1961
Bell, Ernest	Bell's Joy Book	G Bell & Sons	1926
Bendick, Jeanne & Levin, Marcia	Mathematics Illustrated Dictionary	Kaye & Ward	1967
Bennett, Pam	Typewriting Dictionary	McGraw-Hill	1987
Benson, M & E, Ilson, R	BBI Dictionary of English Word Combinations	John Benjamins	1997
Berloquin, Pierre	Garden of the Sphinx, The	Scribner	1985
Black, Donald Chain	Spoonerisms Sycophants and Sops	Harper & Row	1988
Black, Henry Campbell	Black's Law Dictionary (4th ed.)	West Publishing	1951
Blair, J H	Glossary of Language – Learning Terms, A	Blackie & Sons	1963
Blamires, Harry	Cassell Guide to Common Errors in English	Cassell	1997
Blamires, Harry	Penguin Guide to Plain English, The	Penguin	2000
Blamires, Harry	Queen's English, The	Bloomsbury	1994
Blatner, David	Joy of ϖ, The	Allen Lane	1997
Bliss, Alan	Dictionary of Foreign Words and Phrases in Current English, A	Routledge & Kegan	1966
Blyth, Jonathan	Law of the Playground – A Puerile and Disturbing Dictionary of Playground Insults and Games	Ebury Press	2004
Boatner, M T & Gates, J E	Dictionary of American Idioms, A	Barrons	1977
Bodmer, Frederick	Loom of Language, The	Allen & Unwin	1943
Borgmann, Dmitri	Language on Vacation	Charles Scribner's Sons	1965
Borowski, E J & Borwein, J M	Collins Dictionary of Mathematics	HarperCollins	2002
Borowski, E J & Borwein, J M	Collins Internet-linked Dictionary of Mathematics	Collins	2005
Borror, Donald J	Dictionary of Word Roots and Combining Forms	N P Publication	1971
Boycott, Rosie	Batty, Bloomers and Boycott	Hutchinson	1982
Bragg, Melvin	Adventure of English, The	Sceptre	2003
Brandreth, Gyles	Wordplay	Severn House	1982
Brandreth, Gyles	Big Book of Puzzles and Games, The	Treasure Press	1976
Brandreth, Gyles	Classic Puzzles	J M Dent	1985
Brandreth, Gyles	Complete Puzzler, The	Robert Hale	1982
Brandreth, Gyles	Everyman's Classic Puzzles	JM Dent	1985
Brecher, Erwin	Journey Through Puzzleland	Pan Books	1994

Brewer, E. Cobham	Brewer's Dictionary of Phrase and Fable (Millennium ed.)	Cassell	1999
Brook, G L	Words in Everyday Life	MacMillan	1983
Brooke, Maxey	150 Puzzles in Crypt-Arithmetic	Dover	1969
Brown, Hugh & Margaret	Speller's Companion, A	Brown & Brown	1990
Brown, Ivor	Words on the Level	Bodley Head	1973
Bryant, Margaret M	Current American Usage	Funk & Wagnalls	1962
Bryson, Bill	Made in America	Minerva	1994
Bryson, Bill	Mother Tongue	Penguin	1990
Bryson, Bill	Penguin Dictionary of Troublesome Words, The	Viking	1987
Buchan, Jamie	As Easy As PI – Stuff about Numbers That Isn't (Just) Maths	Michael O'Mara Books	2015
Buchanan-Brown, J & others	Le Mot Juste	Kogan Page	1980
Bunch, Brian	Mathematical Fallacies and Paradoxes	Dover	1997
Burchfield R, Weiner ESC & HJ	Oxford Guide to the English Language, The	Guild	1984
Burchfield, Robert	Spoken Word, The	BBC	1981
Burchfield, R W	Fowler's Modern English Usage, The New	Oxford	1996
Burchfield, Robert	English Language, The	OUP	1985
Burchfield, Robert	Unlocking The English Language	Faber & Faber	1989
Burnside, Julian	Word Watching – Field Notes from an Amateur Philologist	Scribe Publications	2005
Butter, Henry	Etymological Spelling-Book and Expositor	Longmans and Co	1877
Butterfield, Jeremy	Damp Squid – The English Language Laid Bare	Oxford University Press	2008
Byrne, Josefa Heifetz	Mrs. Byrne's Dictionary of Unusual, Obscure & Preposterous Words	Granada	1979
Byrne, Mary	Eureka – A Dictionary of Latin and Greek Elements in English Words	David & Charles	1987
Campbell, Grant	Words – A Potpourri of Fascinating Origins	Capra Press	1992
Carey, G V	Mind The Stop	Cambridge U.P.	1948
Carney, F and Waite, M, (Eds.)	Penguin Pocket English Thesaurus, The	Penguin	1988
Carroll, Lewis	Pillow Problems and a Tangled Tale	Dover	1958
Chadsey, C, William Morris, H. Wentworth (Eds.)	Words: The New Illustrated Dictionary	Spring Books	1956
Chalker, S & Weiner E	Oxford Dictionary of English Grammar, The	BCA	1994
Chantrell, Glynnis	Oxford Dictionary of Word Histories, The	Oxford	2002
Ciardi, John	Browser's Dictionary, A – A Compendium of Curious Expressions & Intriguing Facts	Harper & Row	1980

Ciardi, John	Second Browser's Dictionary, A – and Native's Guide to the Unknown American Language	Harper & Row	1983
Claiborne, Robert	Roots of English, The	Times Books	1989
Clapham, Christopher	Concise Oxford Dictionary of Mathematics,The	Oxford	1990
Clark, Sandra	Shakespeare Dictionary	Hutchinson	1986
Clarke, L H	Fun With Figures	Heinemann	1962
Cochrane, James	Penguin Dictionary Game Dictionary, The	Penguin	1992
Cochrane, James	Between You and I – A Little Book of Bad English	Icon Books	2004
Collings, Rex	Crash of Rhinoceroses, A	Bellew	1992
Collins, F H	Authors' & Printers' Dictionary (6th ed.)	Humphrey Milford	1928
Collins, V H	Book of English Idioms, A	Longmans	1956
Collins, V H	Choice of Words, The	Longmans	1953
Collins, V H	One Word and Another	Longmans	1954
Cook, Vivian	Accomodating Brocolli in the Cemetary – or Why Can't Anybody Spell?	Profile Books	2004
Copley, J	Shift of Meaning	Oxford University Press	1961
Cowie, A O & Mackin, R	Oxford Dictionary of Current Idiomatic English (vol. 1)	OUP	1975
Cowie, A O & Mackin, R	Oxford Dictionary of Current Idiomatic English (vol. 2) (with McCraig IR)	OUP	1986
Cresswell, Julia	Insect that Stole Butter? Oxford Dictionary of Word Origins	Oxford University Press	2009
Crilly, Tony	50 Mathematical Ideas You Really Need to Know	Quercus	2007
Crowther, John	Crowther's Encyclopaedia of Phrases and Origins	John Crowther	1946
Crump, Thomas	Anthropology of Numbers, The	Cambridge Uni Press	1990
Crystal, David	Cambridge Encyclopaedia of Language, The	Cambridge	1991
Crystal, David	Language Play	Penguin	1998
Crystal, David	Little Book of Language, A	Yale University Press	2010
Crystal, David	Stories of English, The	Penguin	2005
Crystal, David	What is Linguistics?	Edward Arnold	1969
Crystal, David & Crystal, Ben	Shakespeare's Words – A Glossary & Language Comparison	Penguin	2002
Cuddon, J A	Dictionary of Literary Terms	Penguin	1986
Cunliffe, R J	Blackie's Compact Etymological Dictionary	Blackie & Son	1935
Curtis, John Charles	Manual of English Etymology, A	Simpkin, Marshall Hamilton, Kent	1895
Daintith, James	Dictionary of Mathematics	Intercontinental	1981
Daintith, John (Ed.)	Bloomsbury Anagram Finder	Bloomsbury	2004

Dalton, O & Jolliffe, G	The Whole Hog – Odd Phrases and Idioms Explained	Corgi	1987
Darton, M & Clark, J	Dent Dictionary of Measurement, The	J M Dent	1994
Davies, Alan	Language & Learning in Early Childhood	Heinemann	1977
Davies, Lyn	A is for Ox	Ottakar's	2004
Davis, Morton D	Game Theory	Basic Books	1970
De Bono, Edward	Wordpower	Pierrot	1977
Dear, I C B (Compiler)	Oxford English – A Guide to the Language	Guild	1986
Degrazia, Joseph	Maths is Fun	Allen & Unwin	1949
Dent, Susie	Fanboys and Overdogs – The Language Report	Oxford	2005
Dent, Susie	The Language Report	Oxford	2003
Deutsch, Guy	Through the Language Glass – How Words Colour Your World	William Heinemann	2010
Devi, Shakuntala	Joy of Numbers, The	Coronet	1979
Dickson, Heather (Ed.)	Brain-Boosting Cryptic Puzzles	Lagoon Books	2000
Dickson, Paul	Connoisseur's Collection of Old and New, Weird and Wonderful, Useful and Outlandish Words	Arena	1983
Dillon-Malone, Aubrey	Cynic's Dictionary, The	Prion	1998
Donald, Graeme	Dictionary of Modern Phrase	Simon & Schuster	1994
Donaldson, G & Setterfield, S	Why Do We Say That?	David & Charles	1986
Donaldson, Graham & Ross, M	Complete Why Do We Say That?, The	David & Charles	1991
Donald, James (Ed.)	Chambers's Etymological English Dictionary of the English Language	W & R Chambers	1867
Drabble, Margaret (Ed.)	Oxford Companion to English Literature, The	Oxford	1985
Dudeney, Henry Ernest	536 Puzzles and Curious Problems	Souvenir Press	1967
Dudeney, Henry Ernest	Amusements in Mathematics	Nelson	1917
Dudeney, Henry Ernest	Canterbury Puzzles, The	Nelson	1919
Dudeney, Henry Ernest	Modern Puzzles	C Arthur Pearson	1936
Dudeney, Henry Ernest	Puzzle Mine, A	Nelson	1934
Dudeney, Henry Ernest	Puzzles and Curious Problems	Nelson	1931
Dunbar, Robin	Grooming, Gossip and the Evolution of Language	Faber & Faber	1996
Dunkling, Leslie	Dictionary of Days, A	Routledge	1988
Dunkling, Leslie	Dictionary of Epithets & Terms of Address	Routledge	1990

Dunkling, Leslie	Guinness Book of Curious Words, The	Guinness	1994
Eastaway, Rob & Wyndham, J	Why Do Buses Come in Threes?	Allen Lane	1999
Eastaway, Robert	Enigmas	Arlington Books	1982
Easterway, Rob & Haigh, John	How Long Is a Piece of String? – More Hidden Mathematics of Everyday Life	Robson Books	2007
Eckler, Ross	Making the Alphabet Dance	St Martin's Griffin	1996
Edelstein, Stewart	Dubious Doublets – A Delightful Compendium of Unlikely Word Pairs of Common Origin	Wiley	2003
Edmonds, David	Oxford Reverse Dictionary, The	Oxford	1999
Edwards, Gillian	Hogmanay and Tiffany	Geoffrey Bles	1979
Ehrlich, Eugene	Dictionary of Latin Tags and Phrases, A	Guild Publishing	1991
Elmes, Simon & Rosen, Michael	Word of Mouth	Oxford University Press	2002
Elster, Charles Harrington	The Big Book of Beastly Mispronunciations	Houghton Mifflin	1999
Emmet, E R	Diversity of Puzzles, A	Barnes & Noble	1977
Emmet, E R	Island of Imperfection Puzzle Book, The	Barnes & Noble	1980
Enright, Dominic	In Other Words	Michael O'Mara Books	2005
Espy, Willard R	Almanac of Words at Play, An	Clarkson N Potter	1975
Espy, Willard R	Another Almanac of Words At Play	Andre Deutsch	1981
Espy, Willard R	Game of Words, The	Readers Union	1971
Espy, Willard R	Garden of Eloquence, The – A Rhetorical Bestiary	Harper & row	1983
Espy, Willard R	Thou Improper, Thou Uncommon Noun – An Etymology of Words That Once Were Names	Clarkson N Potter	1978
Essinger, James	Spellbound – The Improbable Story of English Spelling	Robson Books	2006
Evans, Bergen	Comfortable Words	Andre Deutsch	1963
Evans, Rod L	Gilded Tongue, The – Overly Eloquent Words For Everyday Things	Writers' Digest Books	2006
Evans, Stephen & Whitelaw, Ian	Back to School for Grown-Ups	New Burlington Books	2010
Ewart, Neil	Cassell Everyday Phrases – Their Origins and Meanings	Cassell	1991
Ewart, Neil	Everyday Phrases	Blandford	1984
Farb, Peter	Word Play – What Happens When People Talk	Coronet	1974
Farkas, Anna (Compiler)	Oxford Dictionary of Catchphrases, The	Oxford	2002
Farrow, Jane (Ed.)	Wanted Words	Stoddart	2000
Feldman, David	Who Put the Butter into Butterfly	Harper & Row	1989
Fennell, C A M	Stanford Dictionary of Anglicised Words and Phrases, The	Cambridge	1892

Fergusson, Rosalind	New Penguin Dictionary of Abbreviations, The	Penguin	2000
Fergusson, Rosalind	Penguin Rhyming Dictionary, The (English Reference Collection)	Penguin	2000
Fergusson, Rosalind (Ed.)	Penguin A-Z Thesaurus, The	Penguin	2001
Fisher, John (Ed.)	Magic of Lewis Carroll, The	Penguin	1981
Flavell, Linda & Roger	Dictionary of Word Origins	Kyle Cathie	1996
Flavell, Linda & Roger	The Chronology of Words and Phrases – A Thousand Years in the History of English	Kyle Cathie	1999
Flexner, S B	Random House Dictionary of The English Language	Random House	1987
Follett, Wilson	Modern American Usage	Longmans	1966
Forsyth, Mark	Etymologicon, The	Icon Books	2011
Forsyth, Mark	Horologicon, The – A Day's Jaunt Through the Lost Words of the English Language	Icon Books	2012
Fowler, H W & F G	King's English, The	Wordsworth	1993
Fowler, H G & Russell, N	Wealth of Words, A	MacMillan	1965
Fowler, Roger (Ed.)	Dictionary of Modern Critical Terms, A	Routledge & Kegan Paul	1973
Foyle, Christopher	Foyle's Philavery – Treasury of Unusual Words, A	Chambers	2006
Franklyn, Julian	Dictionary of Rhyming Slang, The	Routledge	1971
Franklyn, Julian	Which Witch – Being A Grouping of Phonetically Compatible Words	Dorset Press	1966
Freeman, Morton S	Story Behind The Word, The	ISI Press	1985
Freeman, William	Concise Dictionary of English Idioms, A	English Universities	1951
Freeman, William	Dictionary of Fictional Characters	J M Dent	1973
Friedland, Aaron J	Puzzles in Math and Logic	Dover Publications	1970
Friedlander, K J and Fine, P A	The Grounded Expertise Components Approach in the Novel Area of Cryptic Crossword Solving	Frontiers in Psychology	2016
Frohlichstein, Jack	Mathematical Fun Games and Puzzles	Dover	1967
Fujimura, Kobon (Ed. Martin Gardner)	Tokyo Puzzles, The	Frederick Muller	1979
Fults, John Lee	Magic Squares	Open Court	1974
Funk, Charles Earl	Heavens to Betsy! And Other Curious Sayings	Harper & Row	1986
Funk, Charles Earl	Hog On Ice and Other Curious Expressions, A	John Murray	1950
Funk, Charles Earl	Thereby Hangs A Tale	Harper & Row	1985
Funk, Wilfred	Word Origins and their Romantic Stories	Bell Publishing	1978
Games, Alex	Balderdash & Piffle – The stories behind our most intriguing words and phrases (2nd series)	BBC Books	2007
Gamow, George & Stern, M	Puzzle-Math	MacMillan	1958

Gardner, Kay	Collins Maths Dictionary (2nd ed.)	Collins Educational	1993
Gardner, Martin	Ambidextrous Universe, The	Penguin	1979
Gardner, Martin	Annotated Alice, The	Penguin	1985
Gardner, Martin	Further Mathematical Diversions	Penguin	1979
Gardner, Martin	Mathematical Carnival	Oxford University Press	1987
Gardner, Martin	Mathematical Circus	Allen Lane	1982
Gardner, Martin	Mathematical Magic Show	Allen & Unwin	1977
Gardner, Martin	Mathematical Puzzles and Diversions	Penguin	1973
Gardner, Martin	Mathematical Puzzles of Sam Loyd	Dover	1959
Gardner, Martin	Mathematical Puzzling		
Gardner, Martin	More Mathematical Puzzles and Diversions	Penguin	1971
Gardner, Martin	More Mathematical Puzzles of Sam Loyd	Dover	1960
Gardner, Martin	Science Puzzles	MacMillan	1962
Gardner, Martin	Space Puzzles	G Bell & Sons	1971
Gardner, Martin	Unexpected Hanging, The and other Mathematical Diversions	Chicago Press	1991
Garg, Anu	A Word a Day – A Romp through Some of the Most Unusual and Intriguing Words in English	Wiley	2003
Garg, Anu	The Dord, the Diglot, and an Avocado or Two – Hidden Lives and Strange Origins of Common and Not-so-Common Words	Plume	2007
Garrison, Webb	Why You Say It – The Fascinating Stories Behind Over 600 Everyday Words and Phrases	Rutledge Hill Press	1992
Gause, John T	Complete Word Hunter, The	Thomas Y Crowell	1955
Gibson, Carol (Ed.)	Dictionary of Mathematics	Intercontinental	1981
Glazier, Stephen	Random House Word Menu	Ballantine Books	1992
Glazier, Stephen	Word Menu	Random House/ Webster	1992
Glynne-Jones, Tim	Book of Words, The – An Entertaining Look at Words and How We Have Come to Use Them	Arcturus	2008
Golick, Margie	Playing With Words	Pembroke	1987
Gooden, Philip	Faux Pas? A No-Nonsense Guide to Words and Phrases from Other Languages	A & C Black	2005
Gooden, Philip	Who's Whose? A No-Nonsense Guide to Easily Confused Words	Bloomsbury	2004
Gorell, Lord (Sup. Ed.)	English Language and Literature	Odhams Press	!955?
Gowers, Sir Ernest	ABC of Plain Words	HMSO	1951
Gowers, Sir Ernest	Complete Plain Words, The (revised by Sidney Greenbaum & Janet Whitcut)	HMSO	1986
Graham, William	Exercises on Etymology	W & R Chambers	1865?

Grambs, David	Did I Say Something Wrong?	Plume, Penguin	1993
Gramley, Stephan	History of English, The An Introduction	Routledge	2012
Gray, Martin	Dictionary of Literary Terms, A	York Handbooks	1999
Green, Jonathon	Cassell's Dictionary of Slang (2nd ed.)	Weidenfeld & Nicholson	2005
Green, Jonathon	Cassell's Rhyming Slang	Cassell	2000
Green, Jonathon	Chasing The Sun – Dictionary Makers and The Dictionaries They Made	Pimlico	1997
Green, Jonathon	Dictionary of Contemporary Slang, The	Pan	1984
Green, Jonathon	Newspeak: Dictionary of Jargon, A	Routledge	1987
Green, Jonathon	Slang Down the Ages	Kyle Cathie	1994
Green, Jonathon	Slang Thesaurus, The	Penguin	1986
Greenbaum, Sidney	Introduction to English Grammar, An	Longman	1992
Greenman, Robert & Carol	More Words That Make a Difference	Levenger Press	2007
Grierson, Herbert	Rhetoric and English Composition (2nd ed.)	Oliver & Boyd	1945
Grose, Captain Francis	Classical Dictionary of the Vulgar Tongue, The (ed. Partridge)	Routledge	1963
Hale, Constance (Ed.)	Wired Style-Principles of English Usage in the Digital Age	Hard Wired	1996
Hargrave, Basil	Origins and Meanings of Popular Phrases and Names, The	T Werner Laurie	1948
Hargraves, Orin	Mighty Fine Words and Smashing Expressions	Oxford University Press	2003
Harker, Jillian	Dictionary Word Games	Ladybird	!990?
Harris W T (Ed.)	Webster's New International Dictionary of the English Language (2 vols.)	G Bell	1911
Harris, Cyril M	What's In a Name? – Origins of Station Names on the London Underground (3rd ed.)	Archway	1990
Hartrampf, Gustavus	Hartrampf's Vocabularies	Psychology Pub.	1946
Hayakawa, S I	Language in Action	Harcourt Brace	1941
Hayakawa, S I (Ed.)	Use and Misuse of Language, The	Fawcett	1962
Heller, L Humez, A & Dror, M	Private Lives of English Words	Routledge & Kegan Paul	1984
Hellweg, Paul	Weird and Wonderful Words	David & Charles	1986
Hellweg, Paul	Wordsworth Book of Intriguing Words, The	Wordsworth	1993
Hendrickson, Robert	Encyclopaedia of Word and Phrase Origins, The	MacMillan	1987
Hendrickson, Robert	Ladybugs, Tiger Lilies & Wallflowers	Prentice Hall	1993
Henry, Laurie	Fiction Dictionary, The	Story Press	1995
Herbert, A P	What a Word	Methuen	1959
Herbruck, Wendell	Word Histories	Clarendon Press	1935
Higgins, Peter M	Mathematics for the Curious	Oxford	1998

Hill, Robert H	Dictionary of Difficult Words, The	Arrow	1985
Hill, Robert H	Jarrold's Dictionary of Difficult Words (3rd ed.)	Jarrold	1948
Hill, Robert J	Dictionary of False Friends, A	Meeds	1982
Hitchings, Henry	Secret Lives of Words, The	John Murray	2009
Hitt, Jack	In a Word	Dell	1992
Hoad, T F (Ed.)	Concise Oxford Dictionary of English Etymology, The	Oxford	1986
Hoad, T F (Ed.)	Concise Oxford Dictionary of Word Origins, The (OWLP)	Guild	1989
Hollands, Roy	Dictionary of Mathematics, A	Longman	1980
Hornby, A S	Guide to Patterns & Usage in English	Oxford	1953
Horwill, H W	Dictionary of Modern American Usage, The	Oxford	1946
Howard, Godfrey	Good English Guide, The	Pan MacMillan	1993
Howard, Godfrey	Guide to Good English in the 1980s	Pelham Books	1985
Howard, Godfrey	MacMillan Good English Handbook	MacMillan	1997
Howard, Philip	A Word in Time	Sinclair-Stevenson	1990
Howard, Philip	New Words For Old	Hamish Hamilton	1977
Howard, Philip	State of The Language, The	Hamish Hamilton	1984
Howard, Philip	Weasel Words	Hamish Hamilton	1978
Howard, Philip	Word in Your Ear, A	Hamish Hamilton	1983
Howard, Philip	Words Fail Me	Corgi	1980
Howard, Philip	Word-Watching	ElmTree Books	1988
Humphrys, John	Lost For Words	Hodder & Stoughton	2004
Hunt, Cecil	Dictionary of Word Makers, A	Herbert Jenkins	1949
Hunt, Cecil	Talk of The Town	Herbert Jenkins	1951
Hunt, Cecil	Word Origins – The Romance of Language	Wisdom Library	1962
Hunter, J A H	Mathematical Diversions	D Van Nostrand	1963
Hunter, J A H & Madachy, J S	Fun With Figures	Dover	1956
Hunter, Samuel	Dictionary of Anagrams, The	Routledge	1982
Hurley, James F	Litton's Problematic Recreations	Van Nostrand	1971
Ifrah, Georges	From One to Zero – A Universal History of Numbers	Penguin	1987
Irvine, Alexander (Ed.)	New English Dictionary	Collins	1971
Jack, Albert	Red Herrings and White Elephants	Metro Publishing	2004
Jack, Albert	Shaggy Dogs and Black Sheep	Penguin Reference	2005
Jacob, Henry	Pocket Dictionary of Publishing Terms, A	MacDonald & Jane	1976
Jacobs, Noah Jonathan	Naming-Day in Eden	Gollancz	1958

James, Ewert	NTC's Dictionary of British Slang and Colloquial Expressions	NTC	1997
James, Robert & James	Mathematical Dictionary (5th ed.)	Chapman & Hall	1992
Jarvie, Gordon	Bloomsbury Grammar Guide	Bloomsbury	1993
Jervis, Swynfen	Dictionary of the Language of Shakspeare	John Russell Smith	1868
Jespersen, Otto	Growth and Structure of The English Language	Blackwell	1946
Johnson, D A & Glenn, W H	Sets, Sentences and Operations	John Murray	1964
Johnson, Samuel	Dictionary of the English Language (ed. Alexander Chalmers)	Studio Editions	1994
Johnson, Samuel	Dictionary of the English Language On the Basis of Walker (miniature)	Milner & Sowerby	1800?
Johnson, Samuel	Johnson's Dictionary (Eds. McAdam, E L & Milne, G)	Book Club Associates	1982
Jost, David & others	Word Mysteries & Histories	Houghton & Miflin	1986
Julius, Edward H	Rapid Math Tricks and Tips	John Wiley & Sons	1992
Kacirk, Jeffrey	Altered English – Surprising Meanings of Familiar Words	Pomegranate	2002
Kacirk, Jeffrey	Forgotten English	Quill	1967
Kacirk, Jeffrey	Word Museum, The (The Most Remarkable English Ever Forgotten)	Simon & Schuster	2000
Kahn, John	What's In A Word?	Readers Digest	1985
Kahn, John E	Right Word At The Right Time, The	Readers Digest	1985
Kamm, Oliver	Accidence Will Happen – The Non-Pedantic Guide to English	Weidenfeld & Nicholson	2015
Kaplan, Philip	Posers	Harper & Row	1963
Kaplan, Robert	The Nothing That Is – A Natural History of Zero		1999
Keessen, Jan	Cardinal Men and Scarlet Women	Marquette	2009
Kelz Sperling, Susan	Poplollies and Bellibones – A Celebration of Lost Words	Penguin	1979
Kendal, Sydney T	Up the Frog – the Road to Cockney Rhyming Slang	Wolfe Publishing	1969
King, Dean	Sea of Words, A (3rd ed.)	Henry Holt	2000
King, Graham	Punctuation – Collins WordPower	Collins	2000
Kipfer, Dr Barbara Ann	Writer's Descriptive Word Finder – A Dictionary/Thesaurus of Adjectives	Writers DigestBooks	2003
Kirkpatrick, Betty	Better English	Geddes & Grosset	2010
Kirkpatrick, Betty	Cliches	Routledge	1996
Kirkpatrick, Betty	Concise Dictionary of Common Phrases	Tiger Books	1993
Kirkpatrick, E M & Schwarz, C M	Dictionary of Idioms, The Wordsworth	Wordsworth	1996
Klein, Dr Ernest	Comprehensive Etymological Dictionary of the English Language, A (unabridged)	Elsevier	2005

Klein, Shelley	Stufflebeem, Brockway & Sturt	Michael O'Mara Books	2002
Kluge, F & Lutz, F	English Etymology	Blackie & Son	1899
Korach, Myron	Common Phrases And Where They Come From	Lyons Press	2002
Kordemsky, Boris A	Moscow Puzzles, The	Penguin	1990
Kraitchik, Maurice	Mathematical Recreations	Allen & Unwin	1949
Laird, Helene & Chalton	Tree of Language, The	Faber & Faber	1957
Land, Frank	Language of Mathematics, The	John Murray	1973
Landau, Sidney	Dictionaries – The Art and Craft of Lexicography	Cambridge	1989
Langacker, Ronald W	Language and Its Structure	Harcourt, Brace	1968
Lanka, Christopher	Guardian Book of Puzzles, The	Fourth Estate	1990
Lanka, Christopher	Pyrgic Puzzler, The	Kingswood Press	1987
Lederer, Richard	Crazy English – The Ultimate Joy Ride Through Our Language	Sawd Books	1992
Lederer, Richard	Play of Words, The	Pocket Books	1990
Lederer, Richard	Word Circus	Merriam-Webster	1998
Leigh, Percival	Comic English Grammar, The	Bracken Books	1989
Lemon, Don	Illustrated Book of Puzzles, The	Saxon & Co	1893
Lewis, Nigel	Book of Babel, The	Viking	1994
Liberman, Anatoly	Word Origins… and How We Know Them	Oxford	2005
Linacre, Vivian	General Rule, The – A Guide to Customary Weights and Measures	The Squeeze Press	2007
Lindgren, Harry	Spelling Reform	Alpha	1969
Longley-Cook, L H	Work This One Out	Ernest Benn	1960
Lukacs, C & Tarjan, E	Mathematical Games	Granada	1968
MacDonald, A (Ed.)	Chambers's Etymological English Dictionary	W & R Chambers	1960
Mackay, Charles	Lost Beauties of the English Language	Bibliophile	1987
Macrone, Michael	It's Greek To Me	Pavilion	1992
Madachy, Joseph	Madachy's Mathematical Recreations	Dover	1979
Maleska, Eugene T	Maleska's Favorite Word Games	Fireside	1989
Maleska, Eugene T	Pleasure In Words, A	Hamish Hamilton	1981
Mallett, Richard	Doggerel's Dictionary	Jonathan Cape	1946
Man, John	Alpha Beta	Headline	2000
Manser, Martin	Buttering Parsnips – The Secret Life of the English Language	Weidenfeld & Nicholson	2007
Manser, Martin	Dictionary of Word & Phrase Origins	Shpere Books	1989
Manser, Martin	Guinness Book of Words, The	Guinness	1991
Manser, Martin	Printing and Publishing Terms	Chambers	1988

Manser, Martin & Turton, Nigel	Penguin Wordmaster Dictionary, The	Penguin	1987
Manser, Marton (Ed.)	Bloomsbury Good Word Guide	Bloomsbury	1989
Marsh, D & Hodsdon, A (Eds.)	English Language, The Guardian Book of	The Guardian	2007
Maxwell, Kerry	Brave New Words – A Language Lover's Guide to the 21st Century	Pan	2007
McCrum, Cran & MacNeil	Story of English, The	Faber & Faber	1992
McCutcheon, Mark	Descriptionary – A Thematic Dictionary (2nd ed.)	Checkmark Books	2000
McDonald, James	Wordly Wise	Constable	1984
McKean, Erin (Ed.)	Weird and Wonderful Words	Oxford University Press	2003
McLeod, William T (Ed.)	New Collins Thesaurus, The	Collins	1987
McMordie, W	English Idioms and How to Use Them	Oxford	1966
Menninger, Karl	Calculator's Cunning	Bell	1964
Meyer, Jerome	World's Greatest Puzzles, The	Pyramid Books	1963
Mikhail, E H	Dictionary of Appropriate Adjectives	Cassell	1994
Mira, Julio A	Mathematical Teasers	Barnes & Noble	1970
Mish, F C (Ed.)	Merriam-Webster New Book of Word Histories	Merriam-Webster	1991
Moore, John	You English Words – A Book About Them	Dell Publishing Co Inc	1961
Morice, Dave	Dictionary of Wordplay, The	Teachers & Writers Collaborative	2001
Morris, Ivan	Ivan Morris Puzzle Book, The	Penguin	1972
Morris, Ivan	Foul Play and Other Puzzles	Bodley Head	1972
Moscovich, Ivan	Hinged Square & Other Puzzles, The	BCA	2005
Moscovich, Ivan	Shoelace Problem & Other Puzzles, The	BCA	2004
Moscovich, Ivan	Monty Hall Problem & Other Puzzles, The	BCA	2004
Moss, Norman	Hutchinson British-American Dictionary	Helicon	1994
Mosteller, Frederick	Fifty Challenging Problems in Probability	Dover	1987
Newby, Peter	Pears Advanced Word-Puzzler's Dictionary	Pelham Books	1987
Newby, Peter	Pears Word Games	Pelham Books	1990
Nicholson, Margaret	Dictionary of American-English Usage, A	Signet	1957
Northrop, Eugene	Riddles in Mathematics	English Universities	1959
O'Beirne, T H	Puzzles & Paradoxes	Oxford University	1965
Odean, Kathleen	High Steppers, Fallen Angels & Lollipops – Wall Street Slang	Dodd Mead	1988
Ogilvie, John (Ed.)	Imperial Dictionary, The (3 vols.)	Blackie & Son	1850
O'Kill, Brian	Dictionary of Word Origins	Longman	1984

Oliver, Harry	March Hares and Monkeys' Uncles	Metro Publishing	2005
O'London, John	Is It Good English	George Newnes	1937
Onions, C T	Modern English Syntax	Routledge	1971
Onions, C T (Ed.)	Oxford Dictionary of English Etymology, The	Oxford	1966
Onions, C T (Ed.)	Shakespeare Glossary, A (enlarged and revised by R D Eagleson)	Clarendon Press	1986
Onions, C T (Ed.)	Shorter Oxford English Dictionary, The (2 vols.)	Clarendon Press	1978
Opie, Iona & Peter	Oxford Dictionary of Nursery Rhymes, The	OUP	1992
Orton, Harold & Wright, Nathalia	Word Geography of England, A	Seminar Press	1974
Owen, Denis	What's In A Name – A Look at the Origins of Plant and Animal Names	BBC	1985
Parkinson, Judy	From Hue & Cry to Humble Pie	Michael O'Mara Books	2000
Parkinson, Judy	I Before E (Except After C) – Old-School Ways to Remember Stuff	Michael O'Mara Books	2007
Parkinson, Judy	Spilling the Beans on the Cat's Pyjamas	Michael O'Mara Books	2009
Parlett, David	Guinness Book of Word Games, The	Guinness Publishing	1995
Parlett, David	Penguin Book of Word Games, The	Allen Lane	1982
Parrish, Thomas	Grouchy Grammarian, The	BCA	2002
Partridge, Eric	Adventuring Among Words	Andre Deutsch	1961
Partridge, Eric	Charm of Words, A	Hamish Hamilton	1960
Partridge, Eric	Comic Alphabets	Routledge & Kegan	1961
Partridge, Eric	Concise Usage & Abusage	Hamish Hamilton	1954
Partridge, Eric	Dictionary of Abbreviations, A	Allen & Unwin	1943
Partridge, Eric	Dictionary of Catch Phrases, A (2nd ed., reprint 1993)	Routledge	1993
Partridge, Eric	Dictionary of Clichés, A	Routledge	1980
Partridge, Eric	Dictionary of Forces Slang 1939-1945, A	Secker & Warburg	1948
Partridge, Eric	Dictionary of Historical Slang, A	Penguin	1972
Partridge, Eric	Dictionary of R.A.F Slang, A	Michael Joseph	1945
Partridge, Eric	Dictionary of Slang & Unconventional English (2 vols.)	Routledge & Kegan	1961
Partridge, Eric	Dictionary of Slang & Unconventional English (vol. 2 only)	Routledge & Kegan	1961
Partridge, Eric	Dictionary of the Underworld, A	Wordsworth	1989
Partridge, Eric	English – A Course for Human Beings	Winchester	1930?
Partridge, Eric	Eric Partridge In His Own Words (Ed. David Crystal)	MacMillan	1981
Partridge, Eric	Gentle Art of Lexicography, The	Andre Deutsch	1963
Partridge, Eric	Here There and Everywhere	Hamish Hamilton	1950

Partridge, Eric	Name Into Word	Secker & Warburg	1949
Partridge, Eric	Name Your Child	Evans	1968
Partridge, Eric	New Testament Word-Book, A – A Glossary	Routledge	1940
Partridge, Eric	Notes on Punctuation	Basil Blackwell	1955?
Partridge, Eric	Origins	Greenwich House	1983
Partridge, Eric	Partridge's Concise Dictionary of Slang & Unconventional English From the Work of EP	MacMillan	1989
Partridge, Eric	Shakespeare's Bawdy	Routledge	1961
Partridge, Eric	Smaller Slang Dictionary	Routledge	1961
Partridge, Eric	Supplement to the First Ed. of the Dictionary of Slang & Unconventional English	George Routledge	1938
Partridge, Eric	Usage & Abusage	Penguin	1967
Partridge, Eric	World of Words, The	Routledge	1939
Partridge, Eric	You Have a Point There	Hamish Hamilton	1953
Partridge, Eric	Usage & Abusage – A Guide To Good English (3rd ed.)	Penguin	1999
Patterson, R, F (Ed.)	Greenwich English Dictionary, The	Greenwich Editions	1990
Paulos, John Allen	Beyond Numeracy – An Uncommon Dictionary of Mathematics	Viking	1991
Paulos, John Allen	Innumeracy	Viking	1988
Payack, Paul J J	Million Words and Counting, A – How Global English Is Rewriting the World	Citadel Press	2008
Peacey, Howard	Meaning of the Alphabet, The	Murray & Gee	1949
Pearsall, Judy (Ed.)	New Oxford Dictionary of English	Clarendon Press	1998
Pedoe, Dan	Gentle Art of Mathematics, The	English Universities	1958
Perelman, Yakov	Figures For Fun	Foreign Lang Pub Moscow	
Phillips, Hubert	Word Play	Ptarmigan	1945
Phythian, B A	Concise Dictionary of Confusables, A	Guild	1989
Phythian, B A	Concise Dictionary of Correct English, A	Guild	1979
Phythian, B A	Concise Dictionary of Foreign Expressions, A	Hodder & Stoughton	1990
Pinker, Steven	Language Instinct, The	Penguin	1994
Pinker, Steven	Stuff of Thought, The	Penguin Allen Lane	2002
Pinker, Steven	Words and Rules – The Ingredients of Language	Weidenfeld & Nicholson	1999
Pinkney, Maggie (Compiler)	Wicked – A Cynic's Dictionary	Five Mile Press	2005
Polya, G	How To Solve It	Doubleday	1957
Postill, Ronald	Sunday Times Brain Teasers	Penguin	1974

Potter, Simeon	Our Language	Penguin	1959
Prebble, R & Griffiths, M	Word File	Keesing (UK)	1987
Prout, W Leslie	Think Again	Fred Warne	1958
Pulleyn, William	Etymological Compendium, The or Portfolio of Origins and Inventions	William Tegg	1853
Pulliam, Tom & Caruth, Gorton	Complete Word Game Dictionary, The	Facts on File	1984
Quirk, Randolph	Use of English, The (2nd ed.)	Longman	1970
Quirk, Greenbaum, Leech and Svartvik	Comprehensive Grammar of The English Language	Longmans	1985
Radford, E & Smith, A	To Coin A Phrase – A Dictionary of Origins	Papermac	1981
Radford, Edwin	Crowther's Encyclopaedia of Phrases and Origins	John Crowther	1945
Radford, Edwin	To Coin A Phrase	Arrow	1974
Rapoport, Anatol	Fights, Games and Debates	Ann Arbor	1960
Redgrave, Olwen	Handbook of English Grammar Usage	Minerva Press	1966
Rees, Nigel	"Oops, Pardon Mrs Arden" An Embarrassment of Domestic Catchphrases	Robson Books	2001
Rees, Nigel	A Word in Your Shell-like – 6,000 Curious & Everyday Phrases Explained	Collins	2004
Rees, Nigel	All Gong and No Dinner – 1001 Homely Phrases and Curious Domestic Sayings	Collins	2007
Rees, Nigel	Bloomsbury Dictionary of Phrase & Allusion	Bloomsbury	1991
Rees, Nigel	Cassell's Dictionary of Word and Phrase Origins	Cassell	2004
Rees, Nigel	Dictionary of Catchphrases	Cassell	1995
Rees, Nigel	Dictionary of Phrase & Fable	Parragon Books	1991
Rees, Nigel	Dictionary of Popular Phrases	Bloomsbury	1992
Rees, Nigel	Why Do We Quote?	Blandford	1989
Rees, Nigel	Why Do We Say...?	Blandford	1987
Reisner, R & Dawson, J	Encyclopaedia of Graffiti	Galahad Books	1980
Rheingold, Howard	They Have A Word For It	Sarabande	2000
Richardson, Charles	New Dictionary of the English Language (vols. 1 & 2)	William Pickering	1836 and 1837
Rising, T Craske	English Through Games	Harrap	1941
Ritter, R M (Ed.)	Oxford Manual of Style, The	Oxford	2002
Roberts, Chris	Heavy Words Lightly Thrown	Granta Books	2004
Roberts, Philip D	Plain English – A User's Guide	Penguin	1987
Robinson, Mairi (Ed.-in-chief)	Chambers 21st Dictionary	Chambers	1996
Robson, Peter	Maths Dictionary	Newby Books	2003
Rodale, J I	Word Finder, The	Rodale Press	1947

Rogers, James	A-Z of Quotes & Clichés	Chancellor Press	1985
Rogers, James	Dictionary of Cliches	Ward Lock	1985
Roget, Peter	Roget's Thesaurus	Penguin	1966
Room, Adrian	Dictionary of Changes in Meaning	Guild	1986
Room, Adrian	Dictionary of Changes in Meaning, NTC's	NTC	1996
Room, Adrian	Dictionary of Confusing Words and Meanings	The Leisure Circle	1985
Room, Adrian	Dictionary of Contrasting Pairs	Routledge	1988
Room, Adrian	Dictionary of First Names	Hutchinson	1994
Room, Adrian	Dictionary of Trade Name Origins	Routledge	1984
Room, Adrian	Dictionary of True Etymologies	Routledge	1986
Room, Adrian	Dictionary of Word Histories, The Cassell	Cassell	2001
Room, Adrian	Dictionary of World Place Names	Routledge	1989
Room, Adrian	Dunces, Gourmands and Petticoats	NTC	1997
Room, Adrian	Hutchinson Concise Dictionary of Word Origins, The	Helicon	1995
Room, Adrian	Naming Names	Routledge	1981
Room, Adrian	Room's Classical Dictionary	Routledge	1983
Room, Adrian	Room's Dictionary of Confusibles	Routledge	1979
Room, Adrian	Room's Dictionary of Distinguishables	Routledge	1981
Room, Adrian	Guinness Book of Numbers, The	Guinness Books	1989
Rooney Dr Kathy (Ed.-in-chief)	Encarta World English Dictionary	Bloomsbury	1999
Rouse Ball, W W & Coxeter, H S M	Mathematical Recreations and Essays (13th ed.)	Dover	1987
Russell, Ken & Carter, Philip	Word Games and Word Play, The Complete Guide to	Foulsham	1995
Sacks, David	Language Visible: Unraveling the Mystery of the Alphabet From A to Z (same as The Alphabet)	Alfred A Knopf Canada	2003
Sacks, David	The Alphabet	Hutchinson	2003
Safire, William	Take My Word For It	Henry Holt	1986
Saussy III, George Stone	Oxter English Dictionary, The	Facts on File	1984
Saussy, George Stone III	Penguin Dictionary of Curious and Interesting Words	Penguin	1986
Sawyer, W W	Mathematician's Delight	Penguin	1954
Sawyer, W W	Prelude to Mathematics	Penguin	1959
Sawyer, W W	Vision in Elementary Mathematics	Penguin	1964
Scheurweghs, G	Present-Day English Syntax	Longmans	1959
Schuh, Frederick	Master Book of Mathematical Recreations, The	Dover	1968
Schur, Norman	Dictionary of Challenging Words, A	Penguin	1989

Schwartzman, Steven	Words of Mathematics, The – An Etymological Dictionary of Mathematical Terms Used in English	The Mathematical Association of America	1994
Schwarz, Catherine (Ed.) & others	Chambers English Dictionary	Chambers	1988
Schwarz, J C P	Chambers Backwords	Chambers	1987
Scott, A F	Current Literary Terms	MacMillan	1965
Sedgwick, Frank	Where Words Come From – A Dictionary of Word Origins	Continuum	2009
Seely, John	Words – One Step Ahead	Oxford	2002
Seidl, Jennifer & McMordie, W	English Idioms and How to Use Them	Oxford	1978
Shaw, Harry	Dictionary of Problem Words and Expressions	McGraw-Hill	1987
Sheridan, Thomas	Complete Dictionary of the English Language Both with Regard to Sound and Meaning, A (2 vols.)	Charles Dilly	1790
Shipley, Joseph T	Dictionary of Word Origins	Philosophical Library	1975
Shipley, Joseph T	In Praise of English	Times Books	1977
Shipley, Joseph T	Origins of English Words	John Hopkins	1984
Shipley, Joseph T	Word Games for Play and Power	Cornerstone	1966
Sholl, Andrew	Bloomers, Biros & Wellington Boots – How the Names Became the Words	Past Times	1997
Siefring, Judith (Ed.)	Oxford Dictionary of Idioms	OUP	2004
Silver, A. Maurice	I Wish I'd Said That!	Robson Books	1999
Silverlight, John	More Words	MacMillan	1987
Simpson, J A & Weiner, E S C	Compact Oxford English Dictionary (2nd ed.)	Clarendon Press	1994
Sinclair, J & Moon, R (Eds.)	Collins COBUILD Phrasal Verbs Dictionary	HarperCollins	2005
Sinclair, J M (Con.)	Times English Dictionary, The	Times Books	2000
Sinclair, J M (Ed.)	Collins English Dictionary (indexed)	HarperCollins	1995
Skeat, Walter	Concise Etymological Dictionary of the English Language, A	Clarendon Press	1901
Skeat, Walter	Etymological Dictionary of the English Language, An	Clarendon Press	1883
Smith, Christopher	Alabaster, Bikinis and Calvados	Century Publishing	1985
Smith, Godfrey	English Companion, The	Penguin	1985
Smith, Laurence Dwight	Cryptography – The Science of Secret Writing	Allen & Unwin	1944
Smith, Laurence Dwight	Cryptography	Allen & Unwin	1944
Smith, Logan Pearsall	Words and Idioms	Constable	1948
Smith, William Dr	Concise Classical Dictionary, The	Omega	1988
Smullyan, Raymond	Satan, Cantor & Infinity	Oxford	1993

Smullyan, Raymond	To Mock a Mockingbird	Oxford University	1990
Smullyan, Raymond	What Is The Name Of This Book?	Penguin	1990
Smyth, John	Playing Word Games	Limited Editions	1995
Smythe Palmer, Rev A	Folk and Their Word-Lore, The	George Routledge	1904
Smythe Palmer, Rev A	Folk-Etymology – A Dictionary of Verbal Corruptions or Words Perverted in Form or Meaning, by False Derivation or Mistaken Analogy	George Bell & Sons	1882
Sole, Tim	Ticket to Heaven and Other Puzzles	Penguin	1988
Speake, Jennifer (Ed.)	Oxford Dictionary of Foreign Words and Phrases	Oxford University Press	1997
Spears, Richard A	Dictionary of Common American Phrases in Everyday Contexts	Orbis Verlag	1992
Spears, Richard A	Forbidden American English – A Serious Compilation of Taboo American English	Passport Books	1990
Spears, Richard A	Forbidden American English Dictionary	Orbis	1990
Speigl, Fritz	In-Words & Out-Words	Elm Tree	1987
Spiegl, Fritz	Contradictionary – An A-Z of Confusibles, Lookalikes and Soundalikes	Kyle Kathie	2010
Stangroom, Jeremy	Einstein's Riddle	Modern Books	2009
Stanley, Bernard	Fun With Figures	Universal	?1938
Stevenson, Victor (Ed.)	Words	Book Club Associates	1983
Stewart, Ian	Professor Stewart's Hoard of Mathematical Treasures	Profile Books	2009
Stewart, Ian	Professor Stewart's Cabinet of Mathematical Treasures	Profile Books	2008
Stewart, Ian	The Magical Maze	Weidenfeld & Nicolson	1997
Stickels, Terry	Mind-Bending Puzzles – A 365 Calendar for 1999	Fred Warne	1999
Stormonth, James	Dictionary of the English Language, A	William Blackwood	1884
Strunk, W & White, E B	Elements of Style, The (3rd ed.)	MacMillan	1979
Stubbs, Duncan	Miscellaneous Puzzles	Treasure Press	1931
Suid, Murray	Words of a Feather – A Humorous Puzzlement of Etymological Pairs	McGraw-Hill	2006
Summers, Delia (Editorial Director)	Longman Language Activator – The World's First Production Dictionary	Longmans	1994
Summers, George J	Great Book of Mind Teasers and Mind Puzzlers, The	Sterling Publishing	1986
Swan, Michael	Practical English Usage	OUP	1993
Tannen, Deborah	That's Not What I Meant!	Virago Press	1992
Thomas, Jonathan	English As She Is Fraught...Or How Not To Be Revolting, Insulting, Filthy, Obnoxious Or Anything Like That...	Wolfe	1976

Thomas, Lewis	Et Cetera, Et Cetera – Notes of a Wordwatcher	Little Brown & Co	1990
Thorne, Tony	Dictionary of Contemporary Slang	Bloomsbury	1997
Thorne, Tony	Jolly Wicked Actually – The 100 Words That Make Us English	Little, Brown	2009
Thurner, Dick	Portmanteau Dictionary, Blend Words in the English Language, Including Trade Marks and Brand Names	McFarland	1993
Tilque, Daniel J	Dictionary of Current English Palindromes		2006
Todd, Richard Watson	Much Ado About English	Nicholas Brealey	2006
Townsend, Charles Barry	World's Greatest Puzzles, The	Quality Paperback	1996
Train, John	Remarkabilia	George Allen	1984
Trask, R L	Mind The Gaffe	Penguin	2001
Trask, R L	Penguin Dictionary of English Grammar, The	Penguin	2000
Trask, R L	Penguin Guide to Punctuation, The	Penguin	1997
Treble, H A & Vallins, G H	ABC of English Usage, An	Clarendon Press	1954
Trench, Richard Chenevix	On the Study of Words (20th ed.)	Kegan Paul Trench	1888
Trench, Richard Chenevix	Select Glossary, A	John W Parker	1859
Truss, Lynne	Eats Shoots & Leaves – The Zero Tolerance Approach to Punctuation	Profile Books	2003
Tulloch, Sara	Oxford Dictionary of New Words, The	BCA	1992
Tulloch, Sara (Ed.)	Complete Wordfinder, Reader's Digest Oxford	Reader's Digest	1993
Turner, Tracey	Disgusting Dictionary, The	Hodder	2004
Urdang, Laurence	Dictionary of Confusable Words	Ballantine	1988
Urdang, Laurence	Dictionary of Differences	Bloomsbury	1988
Urdang, Laurence	Dictionary of Misunderstood Misused and Mispronounced Words, A	Readers Union	1972
Urdang, Laurence	Longman Dictionary of English Idioms (L A Assoc. Ltd)	Longmans	1979
Urdang, Laurence	Oxford Thesaurus, The	BCA	1993
Urdang, Laurence	Oxford Thesaurus, The	Oxford	1991
Usher, George	Shakespeare A -Z – Understanding Shakespeare's Words	Bloomsbury	2005
Vallins, G H	Better English	Great Pan	1962
Venolia, Jan	Write Right!	David St John Thomas	1991
Vernon, Tom	Gobbledegook	NCC	1980
Vigilans	Chamber of Horrors (with Eric Partridge Introduction)	Andre Deutsch	1952
Vine, James	Fun & Games with Your Electronic Calculator	Babani	1975

Vorderman, Carol	Help Your Kids with Maths – A Unique Step-by-Step Visual Guide	Dorling Kindersley	2014
Wagner, Leopold	Names and their Meaning	T Fisher Unwin	1893
Walker, John	Critical Pronouncing Dictionary and Expositor of the English Language, A	Thomas Tegg	1836
Walker, Peter (Ed.)	Chambers Science & Technology Dictionary	Chambers	1999
Waring, Chris	From 0 to Infinity in 26 Centuries – The Extraordinary Story of Maths	Michael O'Mara	2012
Waterhouse, Keith	English Our English	BCA	1992
Webster, Wilbur	Webster's Dictionary Game	Meadowbrook	1987
Weekley, Ernest	Concise Etymological Dictionary of Modern English	Secker & Warburg	1952
Weekley, Ernest	Etymological Dictionary of Modern English, An (vol. 1)	Dover Publications	1967
Weekley, Ernest	Etymological Dictionary of Modern English, An (vol. 2)	Dover Publications	1967
Weekley, Ernest	Romance of Words, The	John Murray	1912
Weekley, Ernest	Words Ancient and Modern	John Murray	1946
Weiner, E S C & Delahunty, A	Oxford Guide to English Usage, The (2nd ed.)	BCA	1994
Wells, David	Penguin Dictionary of Curious and Interesting Numbers, The	Penguin	1988
Wells, David	Can You Solve These (Series 1)	Tarquin	1995
Wells, David	Can You Solve These (Series 2)	Tarquin	1984
Wells, David	Penguin Book of Curious and Interesting Puzzles, The	Penguin	1992
Wells, David	Penguin Dictionary of Curious and Interesting Numbers, The	Penguin	1987
Wells, David	Penguin Book of Curious and Interesting Mathematics, The	Penguin	1997
West, Paul	Secret Lives of Words, The	Harcourt	2000
Weston, W J	Manual of Good English, A	George Newnes	1953
Whitcut, Janet	Penguin Book of Exotic Words, The	Penguin	1996
Whiteley, Richard	Letters Play – Treasury of Words and Wordplay	Robson Books	1995
Whiteley, Richard	Treasury of Words & Wordplay (same as Letters Play)	Robson Books	2000
Whitten, W and Whitaker, F	Good and Bad English – A Guide to Speaking and Writing	Newnes	1938
Willers, Michael	Bedside Book of Algebra, The	New Burlington Books	2010
Williams, Guy	Use Your Head!	Chapman & Hall	1959
Williams, J D	Compleat Strategyst, The	McGraw-Hill	1954
Wilson, Bob	Rucks, Pucks & Sliders	Icon Books	2007
Wilson, Professor R A	Miraculous Birth of Language, The	Guild Books	1941

Wilton, David	Word Myths – Debunking Linguistic Urban Myths	Oxford University Press	2004
Wood, Frederick	Current English Usage	MacMillan	1978
Wood, Frederick	English Colloquial Idioms	MacMillan	1969
Wood, Frederick	English Prepositional Idioms	MacMillan	1967
Wood, Frederick	English Verbal Idioms	MacMillan	1979
Wrenn, C L	English Language, The	Methuen	1949
Wyld, Henry Cecil	Growth of English	John Murray	1925
Wyld, Henry Cecil	Short History of English, A (3rd ed.)	John Murray	1927
Yule, H & Burnell, A C	Hobson-Jobson, The Anglo-Indian Dictionary	Wordsworth	1996

INDEX

NOTES AND WORKINGS